Flowers of the Gods

Paul Hayward

Published by

MELROSE
BOOKS

An Imprint of Melrose Press Limited
St Thomas Place, Ely
Cambridgeshire
CB7 4GG, UK
www.melrosebooks.com

FIRST EDITION

Copyright © Paul Hayward 2005

The Author asserts his moral right to
be identified as the author of this work

Cover designed by Geof Hobbs Design
Illustrations of Medusa, Athena's Ring, the wild flowers
and starcharts by Bryan Carpenter

ISBN 1 905226 11 X

Printed and bound in Great Britain by:
Bath Press Limited, Lower Bristol Road,
Bath, BA2 3BL, UK

Contents

Illustrations

 Bluebell Woods

A carpet of spring's wonder
stretches before me
taking me to a different life
when sandalled feet ran
and played among the trees.
Safe beneath their comforting arms.
Carefree and wild
like the flowers around me
memories of endless days
fill my mind
as the nodding heads of brilliant blue
greet me like an old friend
my life has changed in many ways
since first I came to this place
beauty such as this
never changes.

Linda Watson

ᴎame Iᴎꝺex

Albert Ross

Enormous white bird. Friend of Dick Tater and Hecate, Greek mythological goddess of witches.

Andromeda
(Ann-dromm-mid-ah)

Daughter of Queen Cassiopeia and victim of mother's ambitions. Unpretentious princess. Sweetheart to Perseus. Slender young woman, waist-length chestnut hair that framed an oval face with aquamarine eyes, voluptuous lips and a strawberries and cream complexion.

Andromeda Flos
(Ann-dromm-mid-ah Fl-oss)

Daughter of Flos the 'Flower Girl'.

Andromeda Galaxy
(Ann-dromm-mid-ah Galaxy)

(M 31). A spiral galaxy containing dust and gas clouds and 2 billion stars! Is 'nearest neighbour' galaxy to our own Milky Way galaxy. Even so, it is still 2,000,000 Light Years away.

Arachne
(Ah-rack-nee)

In Greek mythology, the 'Spider Girl'. The word 'Arachnid' is now used to identify any creature belonging to the general family of spiders.

Aries
(Air-eeze)

The divine golden Ram and a star constellation.

Artemis
(Art-emm-iss)

In Greek mythology – Goddess of the Moon. A daughter of Zeus. Loved Orion. Nightly, visited Earth to hunt with him. Accidentally killed him with arrow. Got Zeus to put him in constellation.

Athena
(Ath-ee-nah)

Major and powerful goddess. Daughter of Zeus. Also, Goddess of Human Maidens and friend to Andromeda.

Atlas	The Giant. Father of Electra and her six other goddess sisters living in Pleiades constellation.
Atropos *(Att-roe-poss)*	One of three goddess sisters (The Fates). She cuts everyone's thread of life when time to die.
Aunt Kay	Distant relative of Poppy and St John. Lives in Tevlingorde village. Owner of 'The Pig'. Slim, blue eyed woman, about thirty years old with fair shoulder length hair. Chartered Accountant.
Boudicca *(Boo-dee-cah)*	Wife of Prasutagus, King of the Iceni, a tribe of Britons living on the east side of Britannia. Husband to Queen Boudicca. When he died the Romans threw her and daughters off their lands. Boudicca started a civil rebellion and went on the rampage burning Roman settlements. Eventually defeated and poisoned herself.
Briareus *(Bree-arr-ree-uss)*	Giant with 100 arms and 50 heads.
Cassiopeia *(Cass-ee-oh-pee-ah)*	Boastful, queen. Mother of Andromeda.
Cassius *(Cass-ee-uss)*	Roman soldier and husband of Flos.
Ceto *(See-toe)*	In Greek mythology, a sea monster. Mother to Gorgon sisters – Euryale, Stheno and Medusa.
Cetus *(See-tuss)*	Sea monster sent as punishment by Poseidon to wreak death and destruction. Also a star constellation.
Chimera *(Kie-mere-rah)*	In Greek mythology, a fantastically impossible fire-breathing creature that had a lion's head, goat's body and a serpent's tail. We now use the name Chimera as a word to describe a wild impossible scheme, or unreal conception.
Clotho *(Cloth-oh)*	One of three goddess sisters (The Fates). She spun everyone's thread of life from birth to death.
Comet	Frozen balls of ice and rock. Heated up by the Sun as they pass through our solar system, the ice turns to steam and streams back into a tail.
Constellations	Groups of stars that form patterns in our sky. Named after the gods/goddesses that live there.

Cyclops
(Sigh-klopps)

One-eyed giant.

Delphyne
(Dell-fee-nee)

Dragon with small mind, but big heart.

Dick Tater

Nasty northern king and friend of Albert Ross.

Echidna
(Eck-idd-nah)

Daughter of Ceto and Phorcys (who were also parents to the Gorgons). Echidna was a monster – half woman and half snake. She was mother to the Hydra (appears in Book 2) the Chimera and the Sphinx.

Electra
(Ell-eck-trah)

One of seven goddess sisters living in the Pleiades constellation. Inspiration behind the scheme to plant wild flowers on the Earth.

Eris
(Ee-riss)

In Greek mythology, the Goddess of Discord.

Euryale
(Your-ree-ay-lee)

Gorgon sister to Medusa and Stheno.

Fates (The)

General term for the three goddess sisters – Clotho, Lachesis and Atropos.

Flos
(Fl-oss)

Slight build, long black hair, pale complexion, heart-shaped face and soft brown eyes. Andromeda's street-urchin friend. 'Flower Girl'. Later, wife to Cassius and mother to Paulus Cassius and Andromeda Flos. Great ancestor to Poppy and St John.

Galaxy

A collection of stars, interspersed with dust and gas. Our galaxy (The Milky Way) has 100,000 million stars in it. There are some hundred thousand million other galaxies like our Milky Way drifting out there in the universe!

Golden Bluebell

Divine wild flower planted by the goddess, Mother Nature, to control the four seasons of the year and her wild flowers all over the world.

Gorgons
(Gorr-gone-s)

Collective name for three sisters – Euryale, Stheno and Medusa. Monsters, so ugly, that they turned their victims to stone.

Hecate
(Heck-att-ee)

In Greek mythology, the Goddess of Witches.

Helios
(Hee-lee-oss)

In Greek mythology, the Sun God.

Hera *(Here-rah)*	In Greek mythology, the Queen of the Gods and wife to Zeus. Goddess of marriage and childbirth.
Lachesis *(Lack-ee-siss)*	One of three goddess sisters (The Fates). She chose events that occurred on the thread of life.
Light Year	Light travels at a speed of 186,000 miles per second. In 'one whole year', light covers a total distance of nearly 6 million million miles = ONE LIGHT YEAR.
Mars	In Roman mythology, the God of War. Also a planet in our solar system.
Medusa *(Medd-oo-sah)*	Gorgon sister to Euryale and Stheno.
Mercury	In Roman mythology, the Messenger to the Gods. Also a planet in our solar system.
Mother Nature	Goddess of all flora and creator of wild flowers. Sent by Zeus to create the beauty of the Earth.
Nebula(e) *(Nebb-you-lah)* *(Nebb-you-[lie])* = plural	A massive cloud of interstellar matter composed of gases (usually Hydrogen) mixed with dust. There are over a thousand of these known in our Milky Way galaxy alone.
Nereids *(Neh-ree-idds)*	Sea nymphs and attendants to Poseidon. Rode the oceans on Seahorses. Half maiden, half fish.
Nike *(Nigh-kee)*	In Greek mythology, the Goddess of Victory.
Orion *(Orr-rye-onn)*	Constellation. In Greek mythology he was a giant and a hunter. His father was Poseidon – god of the seas and brother to Zeus. The line of three stars in his constellation represent the belt around his waist.
Pan	God of fields, hills and woods. A prankster.
Paulus Cassius *(Poor-luss Cass-ee-uss)*	Son of Flos and Cassius.
Pegasus *(Pegg-ah-suss)*	Divine winged horse. Also a star constellation.
Perseus *(Perr-see-uss)*	King of Mycenae. Warrior. Well over two metres tall. Muscular physique with wide shoulders and neck like a bull. Thick, tightly curled black hair and a full-bearded angular face, with steely blue eyes. Sweetheart to Princess Andromeda.

Phorcys *(For-siss)*	Sea god married to Ceto and father of Gorgons.
Pig	Black Labrador dog owned by Aunt Kay. Pig-headed, a pig for food and incorrigible rogue.
Pleiades *(Ply-add-eeze)*	Seven star constellation where goddess Electra lived with her six sisters. All daughters of Atlas.
Poppy	Teenage heroine and twin to her brother St John. Slight build, long black hair, pale complexion, heart-shaped face and soft brown eyes.
Poseidon *(Poh-sigh-donn)*	King of all Oceans. Brother of Zeus. Sender of destruction, via the sea monster Cetus.
Prasutagus *(Prass-soo-tay-guss)*	King of the Iceni, a tribe of Britons living on the east side of Britannia. Husband to Boudicca. To safeguard his kingdom, he bequeathed his wealth jointly to his daughters and the Roman Emporer Nero. However as soon as he died the Romans threw the queen and daughters off their lands. Boudicca started a civil rebellion.
Prof. Paul Poultney	Retired astronomer. Lives in Tevlingorde village.
Rose	Mother of the twins, Poppy and St John.
Seutonias Paulinus *(Soo-tony-ass Poor-lie-nuss)*	Roman governor-general of Britannia. Finally put down civil uprising by defeating Queen Boudicca in battle. Poisoned herself afterwards.
Sphinx *(Sff-incks)*	In Greek myth, daughter of Echidna. She had wings and the body of lion, but the upper half was that of a full-blown woman. Had reputation of asking passers-by an unanswerable riddle. When they could not answer it – she ate them! A giant carving of her stands amongst the Egyption pyramids.
St John *(Sin-junn)*	Teenage hero and twin to his sister Poppy. Stocky build, angular features, blue eyes and tousled fair hair.
Stheno *(Stee-noe)*	Gorgon sister to Euryale and Medusa.
Tevlingorde	Village near to Honeypot Hill. Home to Aunt Kay and Professor Paul Poultney.

Vesta
(Vess-tah)

Roman goddess of Hearth and Home. At her temple in Rome, a sacred flame was kept burning in a hearth by six priestesses 24 hours a day. It was the Roman State's symbolic 'home fireplace' for all its citizens across the empire.

Vulcan

Smarmy salesman who seduced Electra's mum.

White Archangels

Common British wild flowers. Created and appointed by Mother Nature as guardians of her wild flowers and the magic golden Bluebell.

Zeus
(Zee-oos)

In Greek mythology, the King of the Gods in the heavens. Husband to Hera, father to Athena.

Introduction

To those it may concern,

FLOWERS OF THE GODS, which is Book One of *The Wild Flower Trilogy*, starts at the beginning of time when the Earth was made beautiful by the goddess, Mother Nature, who planted wild flowers across its surface. She then placed a golden Bluebell on a wooded hill in the heart of England. The Bluebell's divine power held total control over the four seasons of the year and each of her wild flowers all over the world.

It also tells how the gods and goddesses of Greek and Roman mythology played a part in making that happen. However, the selfish actions of some of the gods in that distant past are about to destroy every wild flower and the world we live in today.

Ancient history shows that there were many gods and goddesses in Greek and Roman times. There were also giants and monsters. Some later dwelt on the Earth, but most lived in the heavens in constellations.

Constellations are groups of stars that form patterns in our night sky. Each constellation has its own name. Usually, the star pattern is named after the god, goddess, monster, or animal that lives in that constellation. They can all be seen with the naked eye on a clear night. To help pick them out, star maps of our night sky are included in this book.

CHILDREN OF THE STARS, which is Book Two of *The Wild Flower Trilogy*, will also contain maps of our night sky. These will be needed to follow the teenagers, Poppy Hayward and her twin brother St John Hayward, on their journey through the stars. Due to the squabbles of the gods in the distant past, their mundane lives in our present time are thrown into chaos when they are sent right across the heavens in a dangerous quest to find a way to save every wild flower on Earth. In fact, to save the very Earth itself!

A BUNCH OF WILD FLOWERS, which is Book Three of *The Wild Flower Trilogy*, will include illustrations of the common British wild flowers that feature in the story. The sketches will be helpful to spot them whilst walking in the countryside. Do not look too closely though – lest you discover the golden Bluebell that was planted by the goddess, Mother Nature. No human being could be trusted with the power it holds if they got their hands on it.

Moreover, the pictures will be useful to identify each wild flower that makes its appearance in the story. When Poppy and St John return to Earth from their dangerous journey through the heavens, they alone have to face the greatest evil ever known to mankind. The only source they can turn to for help is A Bunch of Wild Flowers.

 Chapter 1

In the Beginning

At the beginning of time and space the stars blossomed like silver daisies in the inky black cosmos. A dark, lonely planet wandered amongst the comets and asteroids, belonging to nowhere, belonging to no one. Shrouded in mist, it drifted through the endless universe and into the realms of the gods and goddesses of Greek and Roman mythology. The planet passed through the countless star pattern constellations in our night sky, which are the homes of those gods. If you glance at the star maps then look outside your bedroom window, you will see that the truth of this story is out there – all around you.

As fate would have it, the planet wandered into the constellation of the Pleiades. There are seven stars which make up the star pattern of the Pleiades. Each of the seven stars is, in fact, a minor goddess. They were the seven daughters of Atlas, the *Giant.* Previous to dwelling in the Pleiades, the girls lived with Atlas in a small celestial abode (with garden gnomes) on the fringes of our galaxy.

They were a one-parent family and there is a little snippet about that.

It is rumoured that mum had ran off a couple of thousand years before with a smooth-talking, two-headed (and two-faced) Vulcan. Apparently, he had called at the door one day selling dishcloths knitted by Martian veterans who had been disabled in the last inter-galactic war. He assured her this was a genuine registered charity organisation. In actual fact, he bought the dishcloths cheap from a discount store on his home planet, stuck 25% on the price and sold them from door to door across the cosmos. The Vulcan went to great lengths to point out the absorbent qualities of the material, but mum was not impressed by that. She was more impressed with his charm and complimentary words on her looks and figure – particularly after having given birth to the seven 'ankle-biters' that were her daughters. It was wonderfully refreshing to have so much attention paid to her. 'A damned sight different to Atlas' she thought. To tell the truth, she had grown sick to death of him. All Atlas did was pace up and down the living room all day flexing his muscles and never once helped with the housework. Besides that, the last time Atlas had paid her any attention was when she was pregnant with their seventh daughter, Electra, and went into labour. It so happens that it was lunchtime and he was concerned as to whether she would still be all right to get his food ready!

The seven daughters did not help the situation either. They were all sliding into the terrible-teens stage and all the annoying things that accompanied it. You know the sort of thing? The only way mum stood any chance of getting the girls to hang their clothes up would have been to screw coat hangers into the floor. The total mess in each of their bedrooms was like a scene from the wilderness. In the morning madhouse of getting dressed for school, chests of drawers would be half pulled open all the way down to the bottom and clothes rummaged through to find a new pair of knickers. Then they were just left drooping. No! Not the knickers – the drawers! And no! Not those sorts of drawers either! I mean the drawers in the chests of drawers. Anyway, this gave the appearance of a waterfall of underwear that spilled from the top drawer, down into the second drawer and so on in a cascade of clothing that flowed across the bedroom floor, seeped under the door and onto the landing.

The appearance at mum's doorstep of the smarmy Vulcan was the opportunity for her to escape all the drudgery of domestic life and get out into the big wide universe for adventure. So, she ran off with 'old smoothy pants', as her disgruntled daughters bitterly called the Vulcan afterwards. Fifty years and fifty planets later, he dumped her for a Venusian girl, because he fell in love with her five green eyes. Mum wanted to return home, but Atlas wouldn't take her back. He had the arrogance to think that it was he that had been shabbily treated. A lot of goddesses wondered who the hell he thought he was! It just went to show that there were always two sides to a mythological story.

With mum gone and Atlas spending most of his time down the gymnasium – bulging his biceps and toning his torso, the seven minor goddesses had to more or less drag themselves up into adolescence.

It is an interesting story as to how the seven sisters now came to be living in a huge palace, smack in the middle of the constellation of Pleiades, instead of in their modest dwelling smack in the middle of nowhere. It is worth the telling, because when you look up at the night sky and see the Pleiades, it explains how the constellation got there and why there are seven stars in it.

Well, the whole thing started with Orion. Once Zeus had given the immortal Orion his own constellation in the sky he spent his time tearing around the universe hunting lions, tigers, bears and boars, deer, more deer and even more deer. Oh, yes – and hamsters – big deal! Because he was drop-dead-gorgeous he really fancied himself and used to chase anything in a skirt. That is why you did not see any deer in skirts – they had enough trouble just being hunted by him without having to cope with any additional complications, thank you very much! Orion took a fancy to all seven sisters after he spotted them hanging around the Milky Way shopping centre one night and I will tell you why the girls were there in a minute. Once he had seen the minor goddesses, he could not resist chasing them all over the universe, pulling their pony-tails, wolf-whistling and doing all the other soppy things that lads do when they go all gooey about girls.

The sisters loved getting this attention, of course. Well, all except Electra, the youngest of the seven junior goddesses. She had to admit that Orion was a bit of a handsome hunk. However, she decided (particularly after experiencing the mess her parents had made of their lives) that if she had a relationship it must be a meaningful one, with equal partnership, fidelity and total commitment from both sides. Quite frankly, Electra felt that some of the gods inhabiting the heavens would have a go at a kitchen mop, because it appeared to be something slender with long hair. So, having one of them trailing after you was not altogether due to the attraction of your entertaining intellect, or charismatic personality. In other words, pulling one of them was not exactly the achievement of the century and if you thought it was, it is highly likely that you were extremely lonely and searching for some form of attention.

Despite her critical views on the low expectations of her sisters (and the low intentions of most of the male gods) Electra still went out with the other girls to hang around outside the shops looking for talent. After all, she did not want her sisters to cut her dead for being a boring old bag. Nor did she want the piddle taken out of her any more from their hurtful taunts about Electra being a virgin because nobody fancied her. Most nights they each took it in turn to go into the wine merchant's store to do the 'wobbly bit' and get certain prohibited items. You had to be a minimum age of twenty one (thousand) years old before you could buy cigarettes and alcohol, which none of them were anywhere near.

So, they used to try the old scam of doing the wobbly bit. This meant plastering a layer of bright red lipstick on your lips; wearing a bra one size too small to push it all up front; squeezing yourself into a mini-gown one size too tight and teetering on mum's old stiletto high-heels so that, when you walked, it undulated the posterior at the back and quivered the bosom at the front. This, hopefully, made them look old enough to be able to obtain the forbidden goodies.

The shop was run by a decrepit, visually challenged, *One-Eyed Giant* – known as a Cyclops and because of his eyesight limitations the girls did not have to bother with the deception. It was a different matter when his forty (thousand-something) years old Cyclops son was covering the shop. He had a very keen eye and zealously complied with Zeus' 'Under-Age' regulations. However, the carefully applied cosmetics and mature attire of the sister who had been appointed as the 'adult' for the evening, combined with heckling from the other sisters demanding liquorice laces and aniseed balls from the confectionary counter, which they knew the Cyclops did not stock, panicked him some much that the girls got away with it every time.

Anyway, Orion had been screaming along the Milky Way galaxy chasing a couple of deer when he saw the seven minor goddesses sitting on the shop's wall outside Neptune's Fish Bar. Suffering from an overdose of testosterone (he was sniggeringly called 'orny Orion behind his back) the hunter stopped in his tracks. The deer took advantage of the distraction and escaped into a cloud of stardust whilst the girls soon took the place of the deer as the hunted ones. They all ended up screaming and laughing all over the skies. It was great fun – particularly when Orion caught up with one of them round the back of the planet Jupiter to steal a kiss.

Not everyone found it fun though. The racket from all this heavy breathing was beginning to annoy Zeus, *King of the Gods*. He could not get any peace with the girls giggling up and down the heavens whilst being chased by Orion with his weapon dangling and his tongue hanging out. So, in a fit of temper, Zeus grounded the seven girls in the palace of the Pleiades. That is how they all came to be there and why the Pleiades has seven stars that make up its constellation star pattern.

The deer were not too happy about it. They had enjoyed a good rest whilst the sweethearts were tearing around the sky. Now it would be their turn to be chased up and down again by Orion with a sword just a couple of inches from their backsides.

The seven sisters were not too happy either, but they had to bite their lips, because Zeus, being king of the gods, had the power to do whatever he wished.

The minor goddesses kept their heads down for a couple of hundred years, but after that they started to get bored out of their minds. So, they all decided to do something about it – except Electra. She had not been into all the cavorting around in the first place. Since being grounded in the Pleiades constellation, Electra had used the time to get her thoughts together and set herself a career goal. She decided she wanted to move up in the hierarchy and become a major goddess – like Athena.

Electra got stuck into studying for the godly equivalent of the GCSEs and 'A' Levels in the subjects of: **C**elestial, **R**eligious, **A**stronomical and **P**aranormal studies, or **C.R.A.P.** for short. Her sisters wrote her off as a boring old boff and cut her out of their cunning plan to have fun. Now, it so happens that, when Zeus had grounded them all in the Pleiades constellation, he had forgotten that it lay on a well-served public transport route. Every decade (Earth time) on a Saturday night, the Number 49 Asteroid passed by the Pleiades on a late night service to Star City on the planet Uranus, which happened to have the biggest all-night disco this side of the Centaurus galaxy. So, the girls hopped it out of the window and caught the Inter-Planet Rock Express to Uranus and left Electra behind.

Now, by a stroke of wonderfully bad luck (for the other sisters) it turned out that Electra had really got into this learning thing once she had started. The more she learned, the more she wanted to know. Her favourite 'area of particular practice' was planetary development and conservation. She passed her examinations with 'A' grades. Zeus, pleased at her efforts of self-improvement, decided to visit the Pleiades personally and promote Electra to goddess (Class IV). When he arrived and found the others had bunked off, he went absolutely ballistic and dragged them back to the palace.

Although star constellations are the homes of gods and goddesses, they all have complete freedom of movement (dependent upon their status) around the universe if they wish. The star patterns, which make up their constellation homes, are just the permanently fixed fiery representations of their powerful and supernatural presence. In the case of the errant minor goddesses, Zeus reversed this arrangement. He permanently locked each one of the sisters inside their six representative stars in the Pleiades. However, Electra was awarded complete freedom of movement – within the limits of a new Class IV goddess. She felt so proud. Her only regret was that her mum had not been there to witness her achievements. Sadly she thought to herself:

'It is a great feeling to achieve something by your own efforts, but sometimes, it makes it twice as good if you have somebody of your very own to share it with.'

It so happens that on the very day that our gloomy planet Earth drifted through the constellation of the Pleiades, Electra was in her study at the top of her silver palace tower. She was writing up her dissertation for the University of the Universe Degree on the subject of 'Astrophysics and Their Relevance to Godly Powers' when luckily, she happened to look out of the window. At the sight of the dark, lifeless and lonely planet, Electra – now being dedicated to planetary development – went into total depression. She had done some jolly good work on nurturing planets during her two hundred years of academic research, but the picture of desolation before her eyes was way beyond her powers and capabilities. She knew straight away that there was nothing she could do about this one! Her feelings of helplessness and sorrow for the planet's awful state brought the tears to her eyes. She wept and her silvery starlight grew dimmer and dimmer.

Fortunately, Zeus was sitting on his throne in the heavens surveying his glittering kingdom. Suddenly, he leaned forward with a worried look on his face. For, when he had inspected the constellation of the Pleiades, he had naturally looked for his favourite up-and-coming goddess, Electra. However, her proud, bright and shimmering starlight was now so faint and miserable that he could hardly see her. Zeus became anxious and sent for Mercury, the *Messenger to the Gods*. He instructed him to go to Electra and discover what was upsetting her. Mercury had wings on his heels, which could whiz him at fantastic speeds across the universe. He skipped through clouds of pulsing stardust and dodged in and out of long-tailed comets. Then he circled round the great stars of Betelgeuse, Rigel and Aldebaran (see star map) as they hurled huge fireballs from their white-hot surfaces. Finally, he arrived at the palace in the Pleiades and Electra tearfully told the messenger her story of the desolate planet.

When Zeus got to hear the tale of the dark, wandering planet and Electra's sadness, he pounded his fists together in anguish. This sent peals of ear-splitting thunder and eye-blinding lightning reeling across the sky.

"No planet in my kingdom should be dark and lifeless of beauty!" he roared "And I will allow nothing to upset the good progress as a goddess being made by Electra."

Upon hearing his anger, all the stars dimmed in fright, for they knew that Zeus could take the hottest star in his hand and crush it into cold flakes of snow.

Zeus ordered Atlas to take the dead planet on his huge shoulders and hold it there so that it would wander no more. Today, when looking at a map of the world, very few people give thought as to why it is called an Atlas. It is named after the very same giant, Atlas, of whom the ancient Greek civilization believed carried the world on his shoulders.

Zeus then placed Atlas in a shimmering spiral of stars known as a galaxy. There is a myriad of these in the universe. Our own galaxy has its own special name. It is called The Milky Way and that is where Zeus put the planet.

The Milky Way galaxy is a pretty big place. In fact, it has around 100,000 million stars in it! If you glance at the enclosed star charts, a pale band can be seen meandering its way right across the maps. That pale band is the outer rim of our Milky

Way star spiral. It takes a bit of imagination to picture it in the mind, but our galaxy, with its millions of stars, is like a pancake with a bulge in the middle where a lot of those stars are clumped together. So, it has the sideward shape of two fried eggs stuck back to back.

When it is an exceptionally clear night and there is no light pollution (such as street lighting) you can see the pale band, shown on the star map, stretching right across the sky. Once spotted, you will recognise it, because it is like the soft glow of a gossamer ribbon trailing from one horizon to the other. The wispy silver radiance that it gives off comes from the combined light of those millions of stars as you peer right the way through them towards our galaxy's edge. It is an awesome sight and makes you feel like a little ant. Nobody should be bothered if they do not have the latest designer jeans once they have seen that. Who, in the galaxy, would care what an ant is wearing!

Zeus positioned Atlas and the planet in the middle of those millions of stars. Well, not actually in the middle. Our Milky Way galaxy is about 100,000 *Light Years* across in diameter. Zeus decided he would give Electra a little test to see if she could locate them. He informed her that he had placed Atlas and her planet approximately 30,000 *Light Years* from the clump of stars in the centre.

From her star studies, Electra knew that light travelled at a speed of 186,000 miles **per second**.

So, in one second, a beam of light shot forward 186,000 miles.

Electra concluded that: *A Light Year was the total distance a beam of light travelled in* **one whole year**.

When she counted them up, Electra found that there was a massive amount of seconds in one whole year. That meant a massive amount of 186,000 mile leaps that light made in conjunction with each of those seconds in one year.

Electra added it all together in total miles:

The actual distance a beam of light travelled in **one whole year** *was nearly 6 million, million miles.* She realised it was difficult to say *"six million, million miles"* with a mouth full of sweets, so that was why everyone just said: **"one light year".**

Electra multiplied the 6 million, million miles of that *one Light Year* by the 30,000 *Light Years* that Zeus had placed the planet from the centre of the Milky Way. Then she drew a circle with a compass on her chart of the galaxy and located the planet along its line. It was a hell of a distance in miles for a Martian kid to get sent to the corner shop by his mum and Electra decided she needed to keep a close eye on her very own planet in the future.

Zeus was extremely pleased with the academic learning that Electra had demonstrated in solving the test he had set for her and he gave Electra her very own personal comet. Electra used it to scoot around her home patch of night sky in pursuit of her favourite interest in planetary development. The comet was one of those that sometimes tended to somersault needlessly and was known as a 'vomit comet', but Electra soon tamed it.

The lonely planet now had a glittering home of its own in the Milky Way. Any creature (which includes us) that now looked up from its surface would always behold the beautiful sight of twinkling stars in the sky and the faint silver ribbon of our galaxy's edge that runs across it.

Then Zeus plucked a yellow star from the constellation of Aries the *Golden Ram* and set it near to the dark planet. This gave the planet warmth and light on its surface. Slowly, the mist on the planet cleared and it became a bright, cosy place. Zeus also took a small moonstone from the ring on his finger and set it in the sky above the planet and there was silvery light on the planet's surface at night. Zeus sat back on his throne. He smiled and rubbed his hands with satisfaction. This sent sparks leaping into the heavens, which became more comets to swirl and circle the heavens – signalling to everyone the joy of the great god. Looking across to the constellation of Pleiades, he saw that

Electra's star was brightly shining with happiness once more and the sparkling threads of her long silver hair flowed out into the night sky like frosted spiders' webs on a winter's morning.

CHAPTER 2

THE GARÐEN IN THE GALAXY

Electra was very happy, but Zeus was not content with this. He determined that his gift to Electra would surpass anything known in his kingdom before. He summoned the *Winged Horse*, Pegasus, from his constellation in the sky and sent him to fetch and carry the *Goddess of Wild Flowers*, Mother Nature, to his palace. Pegasus was a strong, fast, magical horse, but what made him the fastest animal in the universe was his powerful wings. He could fly and gallop across the sky snorting clouds of stardust from his flared nostrils into the cold night air. These became the swirling gas clouds of the heavens, which astronomers now call Nebulae. His swift hooves would strike the comets in his path, which would send showers of shooting stars raining down through space and the sweep of his wings could fan stars into exploding furnaces.

Pegasus was now on an important mission and he galloped hard through the night with Mother Nature on his broad back. Her fair hair radiated like golden sunbeams from her delicate face. She was adorned from top to toe in beautiful wild flowers. Her flowing gown was made of pale yellow Evening Primrose, woven together with Silver Weed. Her slender feet were encased in the softest Bluebells, whilst her hands were warmed by purple Foxgloves. Around her neck hung a necklace of pink Water Plantains and her earrings were tiny blue Speedwell flowers. Her glory was the crown of deep green Holly and bright red berries that she wore on her head. The fragrant perfume of every wild flower in the universe drifted around her.

Pegasus swept down to the pink marble steps of Zeus's palace and Mother Nature gracefully stepped to the floor as Pegasus knelt down. Zeus gave her juice of Honeysuckle to drink and wild strawberries to eat whilst he told her of his plan.

"That little planet down there, I shall call Earth", he said. "That yellow star, I shall call Sun and that small silver stone, I shall call Moon. I have given Earth the gift of warmth and light and a home in the sparkling glory of the Milky Way galaxy. I would like you, as a special present to Electra, to give Earth the gift of beauty with your wild flowers."

Mother Nature was pleased to be given the chance to create a very special garden in the universe and she danced across the pink crystal halls of the palace – showering Buttercup petals from her golden locks. Gliding onto the back of Pegasus she swept across the heavens to this new place called Earth.

Circling the planet at a gentle canter, Pegasus carried her across the surface as Mother Nature gaily waved her arms to and fro, weaving her magic. First she created the woods and forests with giant Oaks, slender Birches, tall Elms, spreading Chestnuts and elegant Rowan trees. Then she carpeted the rolling hills and sweeping valleys with lush grasses that sparkled like a thousand emeralds. With a tear of joy taken from her sapphire blue eyes she brought forth the oceans and the slow snaking rivers across the plains. Then she created the babbling brooks in the silent dales to feed and nurture her green magic. At the gentle command of her voice, Pegasus soared high into the Sun as Mother Nature prepared to place the crowning glory on her work. Reaching out from his back, she snatched a rainbow from the sky and then bent its dazzling colours into a thousand hues. With ripples of happy laughter she cast the multicoloured glitter-dust to the Earth, creating on the green satin cloth below, a jewelled crown of wild flowers so magnificent that it would be beyond the wildest dreams of any king.

To the damp woods she gave the pink of Angelica, the purple of Foxgloves, the white of Eyebright, the yellow of Goldilocks and Kingcup. To the hedgerows she gave the white of Queen Anne's Lace, the brown of Lords and Ladies with their black beauty spots and the scarlet of the Poppy. To streams and marshy banks she gave the Blue Water Speedwell, the white of Gypsywort and yellow of the Meadow Rue. To the grasslands, she gave the purple of Marjoram, the blue of Chicory, the yellow of Cowslips and the pink of Centaury. Many more wild flowers were strewn across the lands.

"And now", she whispered to Pegasus, "I will set the balance of life so that all my floral jewels will each have their months of glory."

Sweeping her arms across the four corners of the Earth she appointed the four seasons of spring, summer, autumn and winter. To lock this delicate balance in the time and space of the universe, the goddess planted a single golden Bluebell at the top of a hill in a secret wood. The golden Bluebell held the power of Nature and the power of Time to control the four seasons.

To keep watch over her creations Mother Nature planted special guardian wild flowers in the hedgerows and waysides across the land. Because of their special role, she named these guardians White Archangels. Quietly she whispered to them:

"I have appointed you above all other wild flowers to take care of my children of the woods, grasslands and marshy banks. It is your task to watch over them. Above all, even unto the sacrifice of death, you must protect the golden Bluebell from evil."

At that, she sprang upon the back of Pegasus and with a snort from his nostrils and sparks from his flaying hooves she galloped away into the heavens. With the cosmic winds rippling through his flowing mane, Pegasus swept past the great stars of Rigel and Polaris, weaved in and out of the long-tailed comets, along the starry whirlpool of the Milky Way galaxy and through clouds of pulsing stardust to the realms of the gods beyond.

Time trickled slowly by, like the shallow streams, with flashing salmon and chattering pebbles. The friendly yellow star, that Zeus named Sun, smiled warmly down upon Mother Nature's children, which grew and blossomed upon the Earth. The wild flowers sprinkled the hills and hedgerows, woods and copses with the many faces of the rainbow. Truly, these were the *'FLOWERS OF THE GODS'*.

Silently, the golden Bluebell carried out Mother Nature's wishes. First spring came to visit, giving the thrill and promise of things to come with its green buds and warm gentle breezes.

This was followed by summer – fulfilling the promise of spring. It caused the buds to burst into green leaves and beautiful wild flowers. The bees hummed, birds sang, squirrels chased and dragonflies darted. The Earth was indeed a glorious place.

Next came autumn. The wild flowers dropped their petals in readiness to rest and sleep, because autumn had gently told them of winter's coming. Autumn sent its cool breezes to dance amongst the trees and help them to disrobe of their old summer coats. Gone now were the summer greens – to be replaced with autumn's rusty browns. The bronzed leaves of the Sweet Chestnut, the rich yellow of the quivering Aspen tree, the bright orange leaves of the Guelder Rose and the fiery red of the Rowan tree glowed all around. The leaves were then whipped up by autumn's wind into the colours of a blazing log fire that swirled and danced its way across the lands.

Winter quickly followed. He was accompanied by his servants, the Snow Maiden, Jack Frost and the lion-heart of all gales – the mighty, roaring, great north wind. Blasting its way over the hills and funnelling down the valleys, the great north wind was Mother Nature's winter gardener. First it pruned the trees and hedgerows by buffeting and tugging at all the dead wood, snapping it and tossing it aside. This ensured that when gentle spring came again only the strong, healthy branches and twigs would be left to receive her blessing of green buds.

Under the cover of darkness, Jack Frost stealthily crept in to execute his task. His ice-cold, needle-sharp fingers prodded and jabbed at the silent dells and creaking woods. His sparkling touch rid them of all things that might harm them whilst they slept. It withered the petals and leaves that the great north wind had gathered so that they should seep into the good earth, feed the roots of their mother plants and be reborn again as summer's new jewelled crown. For, when one life ends, a new one begins. This was the wish of Mother Nature and silently the golden Bluebell did her bidding in the cycle of time and space.

A cold, whispering breeze heralded the arrival of the Snow Maiden. Her rosy red cheeks, fresh from the caress of winter, shone against her soft white face. The shimmering crystals of snow, that were her hair, cascaded down over her sumptuous white cloak. Silently she drifted down, gracefully bowing her head and tossing her long sparkling hair. This caused the snowflakes to spiral to the ground. Then, with a sweep of her cloak, the Earth was covered with a white glistening blanket that would envelop and protect the wild flowers in their long winter sleep.

And so, time moved onwards; with the soft delicate steps of spring; the proud majestic pace of summer; the slow, restful stroll of autumn and the stamping march of winter. Atlas held Earth with his strong grip in the Milky Way. The warm, golden Sun shone down. Electra sparkled with joy and Zeus revelled in her happiness. All was peace and beauty.

However, the balance of Nature is such that:

For every action – there is an equal and opposite reaction.

For everything beautiful – there is something ugly.

For everything creative and good – there is something destructive and evil.

And so, came

Medusa!

Chapter 3

The Making of Medusa

As told at the beginning of this story, Zeus was *King of the Gods* and ruled the heavens. However, in those ancient times, there were many other mythological gods and monsters that inhabited both the Underworld on Earth and its many seas. One of the *sea-gods* was Phorcys. He married a *sea-monster* named Ceto and they had three daughters known as the *Gorgons*. Their names were Euryale, Stheno and Medusa. Instead of hair, they had a thousand hissing snakes growing from their heads. Their protruding teeth were as long as the tusks of a walrus. Their hands were of cold, bronze metal and their bodies were covered in the green, slimy scales of a lizard. Their facial image was so shocking that anything that looked at them was turned to stone.

Whilst Euryale and Stheno had been born like that, their sister, Medusa, had been born as a beautiful maiden. She revelled in her beauty and spent so much time looking in the mirror that she became obsessed with her looks. Soon, she began to think she was superior to everyone – not just to the loveliest maidens of the lowly human race, but also to the goddesses in the heavens – even the goddess Athena. Big mistake! Athena had a reputation for her beauty, but she also had a reputation for being a bit of a spoilt brat. As a major goddess, she had a lot of powers, but she was young and was liable to temper tantrums. The last thing Athena could stand was competition from other goddesses, monsters (no matter how pretty they looked) and snotty little human girls.

As an example, the following is a bit of gossip about what Athena was once supposed to have done to a human girl in ancient Greece. Well, there was this maiden named Arachne who lived in a region of ancient Greece known as Lydia. Arachne had a talent for being able to spin the finest thread. People travelled from all over the kingdom to watch her spin the thread and to buy it, because it made beautiful slinky dresses. One day, Arachne boasted that she could probably spin thread better than the goddess Athena. In fact, she challenged the goddess to come down to Earth for a contest. Athena was jealous of the girl's talent and also, more to the point, was a little bit frightened that she might lose the competition. It was fine for Athena to 'Queen-it' up and down in the heavens over everyone else, but when it came to facing up to the challenges of real life Athena was secretly quite scared – which is a lot like human bullies. On top of that, still being quite young (she was only 25,000 years old) Athena thought that she should not be held accountable to anyone. So, she threw a tantrum, took the easy way out and turned Arachne into a spider! "Spin your way out of that one, girlie" she sneered – as bullies do.

It is difficult to believe that a major goddess like Athena would do such a thing and could easily be dismissed for what it was – gossip. However, if you look in the dictionary for the word: 'ARACHNID' you will see it is defined as the name given to any creature belonging to the general family of spiders. It seems that spiders are named after Arachne the 'spider girl' and it was not gossip after all. So, if you see a spider in the bath, it is advisable that you do not throw your rubber duck at it. It could be Arachne – still trying to send out an S.O.S. on her web-site.

Anyway, returning to Medusa and the obsession with her own beauty. One night she went into the temple that had been built to honour Athena, who was also the *Goddess of Human Maidens*. There, Medusa intended to boast in front of Athena's statue that she was more beautiful than her. Medusa was going to be on a winner anyway, because of what Zeus had done. That is another bit of juicy gossip that just has to be told!

What happened was this: Some time prior to Arachne being turned into a spider by Athena, Zeus had popped down to Earth to the land of Lydia disguised as an ordinary human man. He had heard about Arachne's finely spun thread and got her to make some of it into a gown for his dearly beloved wife's birthday. Some of his story to Arachne was true. Yes. It *was* for his wife, whose name was Hera, *Queen of the Gods*, but it was not her birthday and she was not altogether his 'dearly beloved'. Actually, Zeus thought she was a bit of a nag-bag. He might be the '*King of the Gods*' and could take the most powerful star in his hand and crush it into cold flakes of snow, but boy, could Hera give him some earache. She would always be having-a-go at him, like: "When are we going to visit Artemis?" she would moan. "She is *your* daughter as well as mine you know. And what about that comet that goes streaking past my bedroom window at the palace every night. It's disturbing my sleep! You've been promising to catch it for ages and send it off in another direction and if you think you are going off ten-star bowling with that violent yobo, Mars, then you've got another think coming!" etc. etc.

Hera was right – as usual. Zeus was hoping to slide off across the cosmos to visit Mars the *God of War* and have a game of ten-star bowling. There was nothing better than lining up ten stars and wanging a few thunderbolts down the lane to see how many strikes you could get. The stars did not like it much – being whacked to the other end of the universe and all that, but the two gods thought it was good fun – particularly after swilling down a few thousand gallons of honeysuckle brandy. Anyway, Zeus thought that if he got Hera a new dress it would keep her sweet, then he could go off with Mars.

Zeus paid Arachne a lot of money, which kept her happy, but in actual fact it cost Zeus nothing. All he did, on the way down to Earth, was nip across to the constellation of Aries, the *Golden Ram*, hold him up by his horns and shake the living daylights out of him until a few hundred gold pieces dropped out of his golden fleece. Zeus used to tell the ram it was a sort of sheep-shearing thing and that it was good for sheepie-type animals. Aries never really believed him and decided that, if he ever caught Zeus bending over playing ten-star bowls, he would head-butt him where the stars never shone!

Zeus got the dress, wrapped it, tied it up with a comet's tail, sprinkled it with stardust and gave it to Hera. It did the trick and he was allowed to go ten-star bowling with Mars. Mars was a rotten loser. If he did not win, he ended up with a face like a smacked bottom and went bright red with rage. Zeus even made a red planet, stuck it near the Earth and named it Mars so that he could have a laugh every time he saw it. Big joke for Zeus, but bad news for humans, because every time he lost a game, Mars went off in a temper and took it out on mankind. It was easy enough to find a few stupid, greedy people, stir up an argument over a bit of land and start another war. Mars always felt better for watching a few thousand people hack each other to death. "There's nothing like a good Saturday night punch-up" he used to say.

The problem for Zeus came when he wanted to go bowling again and popped down to Earth to get another dress from Arachne. Too late! In between times, Athena had already thrown her tantrum and it is now known what she had done to Arachne. All Zeus found was this little spider sitting in Arachne's chair. She was spinning away for all she was worth, but not making enough thread to make a dishcloth, let alone a dress for Hera – who happened to be a size 48 and certainly didn't need a padded bra. Zeus was livid. His next night out with the boys was definitely out the window. In a rage he stormed off to Athena's palace. Zeus had thought about grounding the major goddess for a couple of thousand years, but that would not have been much of a punishment. Athena would have just lounged around in bed all day reading *Cosmic*politan magazine, *Thrills* and *Moon* romance novels and listening to pop music. The best way to punish the terrible-teeny, he thought, was to dent her ego. So, he slapped a big, bright red pimple right on the end of her nose and a few blackheads on her forehead for good measure. Fifty gallons of witch-hazel (applied with sandpaper) wouldn't have shifted them in a month of Sundays. Of course, at the same time, the exact same blemishes magically appeared on Athena's statue in her temple on Earth.

Athena was devastated and 'threw a right wobble' but there was nothing she could do. The only thing that might make her feel better was to look around for somebody else to take it out on. As it happens, Medusa's overblown ego put her in the wrong place at the wrong time. For, it was at that very moment, that Medusa flounced into Athena's temple to compare her beauty with the statue and boast the superiority of her looks over Athena's. When Medusa saw the statue's face, she could only burst into fits of laughter. Athena, raging with embarrassment, struck down from the heavens upon Medusa in the worst misuse of her power that she had ever committed. She destroyed any trace of Medusa's beauty and gave her the looks of her *Gorgon* sisters – Euryale and Stheno. Just for good measure, Athena gave Medusa an additional affliction. She made it so that blood continuously oozed from the sockets of Medusa's eyes. "Now you won't need to bother about mascara girlie", sniggered Athena. Medusa caught sight of her own reflection in the waters of the holy fountain and ran screaming from the temple into the night.

What a tale of selfishness, hatefulness, spitefulness, arrogance and jealousy amongst the gods. It makes one almost glad to be human until one looks around at the rest of mankind, which sometimes is not a lot better really. Still, it can be seen where humans got it from. Thank goodness there was still the odd good god and goddess that was around then – and still is today! And thank goodness there was the odd good person in the human race that was around then and others that were going to be around a couple of thousand years into the future – even though it was just the shy young girl, Poppy, and her twin brother, St John. The course of blind hate that Medusa was about to take in the distant past would totally change their young lives in our present time. In fact, it could change the face of the Earth forever!

Chapter 4

The Madness of Medusa

Medusa had run from the temple of Athena and fled to the caverns of the Underworld. There, as all mythological gods and monsters had the power to do, she adorned her underground caves with the finest silk drapes, perfumes, furniture of shining silver and ceilings encrusted with sparkling diamonds. However, the radiance of her surroundings did not dull the hate and loathing for herself that lay deep within. Like anyone else, no matter what you possess – be it the latest computer games, wide screen television, or mobile phone – if you do not have respect for yourself and the love of others you have nothing. As time dragged by, the more she looked in the mirror, the more her loathing increased and the more she paced the dark passageways shrieking her hate. Eventually, the madness of hatred took the Gorgon over; she turned the hate for herself onto others. Medusa came to bitterly loath anything that was beautiful, happy, or good. The urge to destroy those things became her obsession.

Medusa also started associating with some dubious characters. Take her new best friend, Hecate, *Goddess of Witches*, for instance. Hecate had never had a very happy childhood. She was never cuddled and told how much she was loved by her parents. Her father had never given Hecate any attention. He used to sleep all day and go out all night. But, you've got to be fair about it – he was a vampire! Her '*mummy*' was busily entombed in her career. Mummy was the Editor-in-Chief of a monthly consumer guide on magic spells called *Witch Magazine.* Due to her lonely and loveless childhood, Hecate hated any kids she saw that were happy and loved by their parents. She had this massive cauldron and used to cook *suet* puddings in it that were irresistible to kids. She called it her 'Death Pudding', because she put addictive drugs in it and when the drugs took over the minds of the kids they became *suet*cidal.

It is no surprise that Medusa eventually came to hear of the beauty of Mother Nature's wild flower garden that had spread over the whole face of the Earth. She wanted to destroy them all, but there were just too many. Her best friend, Hecate, being *Goddess of Witches* and knowing about magic and all that stuff, soon found out about the magic of the golden Bluebell and how its power controlled the wild flowers all over the world. She could not wait to tell Medusa and stir her up.

Medusa was so pleased that she wept happy tears of blood instead of the usual oozing stuff from her eye sockets. If she could get her hands on the golden Bluebell, she could force it to make winter work all the year round. That way, the Earth would become a permanently frozen snowball and all the wild flowers across the world would wither and die forever. It did not matter to Medusa if the same thing happened to all the animals and the human race as well.

There was just one problem. Hecate knew that the golden Bluebell was up north in the Land of Eng. There was a central region in the Land of Eng called The Miggerlands. Strange people lived there who all thought they were birds, because everyone went about calling each other 'Mi Duck'. The golden Bluebell was hidden somewhere near there. "I can't find out the exact spot", said Hecate "but I know a man who can."

Hecate sent a message to a particularly nasty northern king and told him to locate the golden Bluebell. This tyrannical king was always ordering his subjects around and ruled them by using fear and force. He claimed to come from a royal line of King Edwards. Actually, his first name was Richard. So, combining the name Richard with King Edward, his subjects gave him the nickname of 'Dick Tater'.

The only friend the king had was an enormous white bird that sometimes turned up on the lawn for the odd 'snake and pygmy' pie that might have been chucked out. Very often though, the enormous white bird flew out to sea and showered sailors with bad luck from a great height. His name was Albert Ross. Albert Ross was sent off to the Land of Eng by the king and he spent months circling over The Miggerlands until he spotted the shining Bluebell from the air. It was nestled on top of a small wooded hill just outside a pretty little village named Tevlingorde. Before he left The Miggerlands to report back to Dick Tater, Albert Ross ripped the throats out of several hundred of the strange inhabitants. He was sick of them throwing breadcrumbs at him all the time. What really cheesed him off though was that they kept calling him 'Mi duck'. It was deeply insulting. Firstly, he wasn't 'theirs' and secondly, he wasn't a stupid duck!

As a reward for the information, Hecate turned the northern king's mother-in-law into a Black Beetle. This pleased the king greatly, because he thoroughly hated the 'Nagging old bat!' When he was bored, he took pleasure in putting the Black Beetle on his billiard table and watched her scurry around in a panic whilst he slammed snooker balls round the side cushions. He laughingly called the game 'Pot Black-Beetle'.

CHAPTER 5

MEDUSA'S PLAN OF DESTRUCTION

Medusa spent the day screeching with delight as she made her plans.

Hecate had given Medusa a couple of tips to help her seize the golden Bluebell.

Firstly, Medusa would not be able to touch it herself, because the evil within her would infect the purity of the flower and its magic powers would be instantly destroyed.

Secondly, the capture of the golden Bluebell would have to be a covert operation so that no one would notice what was going on until it was too late.

"After all", said Hecate, "There's bound to be one nicey, nicey, kissy, kissy, pretty-pants goddess, who'll get someone to stick their do-gooding noses in if you're found out. If I were you, I'd take a few 'bruisers' with me for back-up."

Medusa's plan cleverly covered all of those things. If she was going to be dealing with the sickeningly pretty wild flowers created by Mother Nature then Medusa would play the same game. The first thing she needed to do was to create her own seeds of evil. She could then plant them amongst the wild flowers at the bottom of the hill where the golden Bluebell grew. They would then grow discreetly amongst the other wild flowers. No one would notice, not even Mother Nature's wild flowers, because Medusa would give them pretty petals and lovely colours. She made five different seeds of evil and gave each of them their own special code name. When Medusa chanted out their names, the newly grown flowers would transform into the creatures that their coded names suggested. At her orders they would then charge the hill and steal the golden Bluebell for her.

She named the first of her evil flowers Devilsbit Scabious. When the time came for her conquest, she would call out that name and those flowers would change into screaming, scab covered Devils.

Her next flowers she named Giant Hogweed. At her command, they would change into giant hogs with bone-crunching teeth and flesh-ripping tusks.

The next flower seed she made and named was the Crowfoot. These would transform for her into long-clawed, razor-beaked, flesh-tearing Crows.

Her next seeds of evil she named Skullcap. These would turn into fighting skeletons armed with helmets, swords and shields.

Her final flowers, she named Deadly Nightshade. At her command, they would change into blood-sucking creatures of the night.

Medusa would command an army of vile beasts. All she needed to do was stand at the rear and direct her army's attack upon the hill to take the golden Bluebell. If anything, or anybody, dared to stand in her way, the vicious army would destroy them. Having seized the golden Bluebell, it could be carried away to the underground caverns of her palace. There, Medusa would have total control over it and Mother Nature's wild flowers all over the Earth. Worse still for mankind, over the very Earth itself!

Medusa obviously needed transport to fly north to the Land of Eng, so she set about capturing a dragon. At first thought, this might seem a difficult task. After all, dragons are supposed to be those huge, vicious, bad-tempered, flame-roaring monsters. However, this dragon was not exactly the macho type that one might imagine. Medusa had already got this one's card marked. To tell the truth, he was as thick as a pudding.

The dragon's name was Delphyne. He lived with his wife in a large cave at the bottom of a mountain. He used to call her 'The old dragon', but somehow it never seemed to sound as insulting as when humans said it about their wives. He never quite worked out why. This gave Medusa a reasonable clue as to his mental ability. Delphyne used to burst into the cave (like big bad dragons do) and roar at his wife: "Where's my dinner woman!"

As usual, back came the sweet reply: "Ya dinner's on ice in the mountain glacier. How the hell did I know what time you'd be back?"

"Sorry dear", Delphyne would whimper, "But...".

"Don't 'but' me ya moron," his wife would hiss at him.

"But I was only asking", Delphyne would whine.

"Shut ya face", his wife would roar. "It's dragons' treat-night on the telly. I'm trying to watch a documentary on the great fire of London – all those lovely flames and burning human flesh and that. Now, PUSH OFF!"

Delphyne decided that one day he would take a deep breath, shut his eyes then 'punch her lights out'. He went to stomp out of the cave in temper, but fell flat on his face. He had tripped over a pile of shiny white human bones. His wife had obviously had *her* dinner and casually tossed the bones on the floor as she sprawled in her limestone armchair. Delphyne used to eat humans as well, but he didn't any more. A lot of them had started reading that posh stick-your-nose-in-the-air *Cosmic*politan magazine with all its flashy adverts. The latest fashion craze for women was expensive perfume. They were splashing it all over and in Delphyne's moralistic opinion were tarting themselves up with it. 'What was it called?' he thought. 'Yes. That's it...Channel Number Five – Odour Toilet – Essence of Paris Sewers, or something like that.' The men weren't much better. They were getting this 'Old Lice for Men' aftershave. "Or is it 'Old Men for Lice'?", he muttered to himself. Whatever it was called did not matter, because the chemicals in both products brought Delphyne out in a rash in a place where he daren't show his mum. So, humans were off his menu.

Delphyne gazed down at the pile of bones again that he had fallen over. "Look at this damned mess", he grumbled. "What do I keep servants for?" The servants he referred to were several mountain dwarfs that scurried around in terror as they waited on his wife hand and claw. The dwarf servants were small in stature and Delphyne sarcastically called them his 'Micro-slaves'. Delphyne dragged himself up off the floor. "You, you little runt, come here!" A dwarf hurried across. "Go to the glacier and fetch my dinner. And hurry up, or I'll roar and singe your beard so bad that you wouldn't even get a job as a garden gnome!" The little slave scurried off. 'Goody, goody' thought Delphyne, 'I'm really looking forward to one of those eye-watering, red-hot curries.'

When the little dwarf slave returned, Delphyne gave a groan of disappointment. It was faggots and mushy peas again. Firstly, he didn't like them very much and secondly they were highly dangerous. They always filled his stomach with gas and he went round trumping all over the place. Once, a stray spark from his nostrils floated backwards and the explosion nearly blew his bum off. Didn't sit down for a week! The faggots and mushy peas were stone cold. He could not possibly eat them like that and needed to warm them up. So he shoved it in the micro-slave. This was bad news for the dwarf. It meant having the food rammed down his throat and Delphyne blasting him to charcoal with a fiery roar. It didn't do the micro-slave much good, but the dwarf-wrapping helped keep the juices in the faggots and stopped the peas going dry.

Such accounts of Delphyne's behaviour may seem discriminatory, but everyone knew of his poor reputation, because it had been in *Witch Magazine*. They had done a research report on the world's most vicious dragons. This was based on how much of a terrible flame they could belch out. The top of the scale started at 'Volcano' grade, followed by 'Blow Torch' grade, followed by 'Scorcher' grade and so on down the line. Delphyne had been placed in the lowest category of 'Puff'. He was livid. He had wanted to sue them for 'De-*Flame*-ation of character'. A solicitor had told him he could go to Zeus's Court of Justice, but if he lost the case it could cost him a leg and a wing. Delphyne said he couldn't afford that risk, because he only had four legs and two wings to his name. The solicitor held his head in his hands, groaned and walked away. Delphyne stood there dumbfounded – wondering what the solicitor's problem was.

Medusa's trick to catch Delphyne was very simple. He was in the habit of going down the valley to where the wood nymphs played near the waterfall. He enjoyed watching the fairy-type creatures skimming back and forth over the surface of the gurgling stream. The sunlight would pass through the cascading waterfall and split into the colours of the rainbow. Those colours would then be gathered up by the flitting gossamer wings of the nymphs and bounced back into the gush of twisting waters. The whole place would become a grotto of shimmering, darting light. It was a scene of vibrant life and shining beauty. Delphyne adored it. Quite often the nymphs would rest by the water's edge and have picnics. Delphyne would eagerly light their wood fires for them with his fiery breath when they wanted to roast hazelnuts.

Medusa had completely covered herself from top to toe by pulling a sack cloth over her head. The sack had one eyehole cut into it. She then hid behind a rock near to the waterfall. Sure enough, Delphyne came down to look for the wood nymphs. Medusa then disguised her voice to sound like a wood nymph. Gently she cooed to him, "Oh! Delphyne, where are yooooou? Come to me and light my fire baby." Delphyne blushed and went all daft-as-a-brush. Happily he trotted round the back of the rock to be faced with a dirty old sack cloth just standing there. Then he caught sight of the one eye staring through the slit in the sack. It was not enough to kill him, but it was enough to freeze him in his tracks. Medusa simply walked up to him and put blinkers over his eyes so that he could only see straight ahead. She then put a bridle and reins over his head and a bit between his teeth. The bit was made of barbed wire. By the time Delphyne had recovered his senses, Medusa was sitting astride his back with the barbed wire bit ripping up into the sides of his mouth. Delphyne went to turn his head to see who it was that had done this horrible thing to him, but Medusa hissed in his ear:

"If you want to live, you scummy little newt, I would advise you not to look, because you are dealing with a *Gorgon*. We are going on a long journey now, so say goodbye to your little friends."

Delphyne looked around the grotto. The soft sandy beach that bordered the stream was now covered in boulders. These boulders had been the flitting nymphs that had caught sight of Medusa then turned to rocks and plummeted to the shore below. Those nymphs that had been gliding over the waterfall at the time had plunged as stones to form a dam at the waterfall's mouth. As the water no longer fell, the stream below had dried up and the shimmering light had disappeared. The fairy dell had become a shadowy place of death. Delphyne knew, without doubt, that he was indeed a slave to the dreaded Medusa. A tear trickled from his eye, but before it had time to roll to the end of his smouldering nose, Medusa stabbed deep into the soft sides of his belly with her clawed feet and yanked the barbed wire bit high into his bleeding cheeks. Delphyne reared up in pain as Medusa set him in flight on a course to the Land of Eng.

CHAPTER 6

SOWING THE SEEDS OF DOOM

It was the dead of night as Medusa furiously drove Delphyne through the clouds that hung over the Land of Eng. She rammed the dragon's head forward and he glided down through the dripping, clinging mist to circle over The Miggerlands. It was a bitter-cold winter's evening. The wisps of smoke from the wood fires of the peasants' cottages spiralled from the chimney pots and helped Medusa spot the village of Tevlingorde. Here and there, the tiny flame of a candle could be seen from a bedroom window. Each flickering light gave comfort to those small children that were frightened of the dark. Luckily, such children were too afraid to get out of their beds – let alone peer out of their windows into the ghostly darkness of the night. If they had done so and caught sight of Medusa as she glided over their roof tops, they would have been dead-frightened children.

However, there were those kids who always ignored their nagging mums about: "getting to sleep!" every night. Tittering under the blankets, or playing with their clay dolls and wooden swords, they heard the swish of Delphyne's wings and looked out of their windows to see what it was. All that their mothers found the next morning were little human-shaped columns of stone. Then the women cried and wailed as they cradled the heavy blocks, that had once been their children, in their arms. The lifeless stony gaze of the wide-eyed kids stared coldly back at them.

HEALTH AND SAFETY WARNING

Readers who choose to refer to the star maps in this book then look out of their bedroom window at the night sky do so at their own risk.

The author denies responsibility and does not wish to be taken to court by any parents just because they've lost a daughter and gained a crazy-paving patio.

The fathers of the dead children cursed in anger and looked for someone to blame for what had happened. In those dark days of distant history, folk were simple and uneducated. When anything went wrong that their ignorance could not explain, whether it was sheep dying, or the water well running dry, they blamed it on witchcraft. That would mean a witch-hunt in the village and some poor soul was going to cop for it. Usually, the half-crazed mob would pick on someone who was a little bit different from them. It might be an 'outsider', or someone with an unusual birthmark, or someone with a mental or physical disability. In this instance, they picked on a woman just because she had a deformed hand.

The village kids used to laugh whenever they saw her struggling to pull the heavy bucket out of the water well with one good hand and a twisted one. It was easy for a few nasty, muck-stirring gossips to put it around that the woman's hand was like that, because it had been kissed by the devil. The devil must have kissed her hand, because he admired her. If he admired her, he did so, because she was a witch. If she was a witch, it was obviously *her* that had put a death spell on the children, because they had laughed at her. Seems like a fair-enough conclusion – if you're daft, ignorant and uneducated that is! The woman was dragged, screaming her innocence, from her cottage. She was bound hand and foot and carried aloft by the yelling mob to the village green. Despite her gibbering pleas for mercy, she was thrown onto a huge bonfire and burnt alive.

The worst part is that she was a widow with three young children. Her husband had recently dropped dead with a cardiac arrest. Of course, in those days, no one knew about such illnesses. As far as they were concerned, he had died – end of story. However, his recent death had not helped the woman's case when she had been accused of witchcraft. Everyone knew that he had been having an affair with another woman. It was easy for the gossips to further accuse her of having struck him down with a witch's curse to get her revenge.

The burning of the mother left three small children alone in the world. There were one or two people in the village that felt sorry for them and wanted to take them in, but none of them dare speak their thoughts – let alone actually do something to care for them. They were afraid that the mob might accuse them of being witch-lovers, or even witches themselves! So, they did nothing and shut their minds to the terrible plight of the orphans. The children were driven from the village. They sheltered in the woods and scratched around for seeds and berries. Eventually they died of cold and starvation.

Medusa knew nothing of this. She would not have cared anyway, because everyone was going to die sooner or later when she got her hands on the golden Bluebell. Her spiteful mind was totally focused on sowing her seeds of destruction. As she swept over Tevlingorde, she spotted the small wooded hill just a short distance to the north of the village. Delphyne hovered over it and there, below her, Medusa saw the soft golden glow of the Bluebell filtering through the treetops. Her shriek of delight ripped through the trees and bushes. Rabbits scattered in fright. They looked up as they bolted for their warrens, panicking to see where the sound of danger might be coming from. None of them made it for more than a metre before becoming stone rubble strewn across the hillside.

Medusa brought the dragon to the ground at the foot of the hill. She slid from his back and went off to do her work. Delphyne dare not move. He shoved his head in a bush and screwed his eyes tight shut to avoid accidentally seeing Medusa as she moved about. He did not want to end up as a stone dragon decorating some old castle gateway thank you very much. Medusa slowly shuffled her way back and forth across the wide base at the bottom of the triangular shaped field. Its two sides, which narrowed to a point at the foot of Honeypot Hill, were bounded by dense lines of trees. Carefully she scraped furrows in the soil with her clawed hands and planted the seeds as she went. Only the long ever-widening stretch of the meadow lay between the foot of the hill and the trenches of death at the bottom of the field.

Soon, the flowers of evil would bloom into life to await the return of Medusa and her command to transform into an army of destruction. Her timing was perfect. It was the start of winter in the Land of Eng and snow would cover The Miggerlands to allow the evil seeds time to settle and sleep. Then, with the coming of spring, their green buds would struggle to the surface. Come the summer, the buds would burst open along with all the other wild flowers and no one would notice a thing. All she had to do was wait until next summer then return to execute her plan.

This gave Medusa plenty of time to return to the caverns of the Underworld on her secret island and rest. Having rested, she would still have time to fly Delphyne down to the land of Ethiopia and witness the sacrifice of Andromeda. Watching her put to death would be a pleasing way to pass the time whilst her seeds of evil grew. Medusa had long despised Andromeda for several reasons, namely her beauty, her kindness to others, her love for another and his love for her. It was enough to make any Gorgon vomit!

As Medusa headed home on the cringing Delphyne, it never occurred to her to pose the obvious question:

'If Andromeda was such a nice person, why was she being put to death?'

Chapter 7

Andromeda and Perseus

It was her mother's fault that Andromeda was facing imminent death. Cassiopeia had ambitions for her daughter, but most of them were mercenary ones. The queen was proud of the princess, although it was in a misguided way. However, her pride was well founded. Andromeda was a slender young woman. She had waist-length chestnut hair that framed an oval face with aquamarine eyes, voluptuous lips and a strawberries and cream complexion. She was elegant in her deportment, endowed with intellect and adept at all the social graces. The problem was, her mother could not stop boasting and it was her mother's arrogance that was now going to cost Andromeda's life.

Andromeda was the daughter of Queen Cassiopeia of Ethiopia. Although a princess, Andromeda was not pretentious. She used to secretly leave the palace and go into the city to help the sick and the poor. She would get the palace cooks to make lots of bread to take out to the beggars and cut up her dresses to make clothes for the orphan kids on the streets. One of Andromeda's favourite orphans was a young girl named Flos – a waif of slight build with long black hair, pale complexion, heart-shaped face and soft brown eyes. Flos used to collect wild flowers from the fields and sell them in the city to get money to survive. City women bought them to decorate their hair.

Flos had never known her father. Apparently a small band of Roman soldiers, on their way home to Rome, had been shipwrecked on the beach near to the city of Cassiopeia's realm.

Flos's mother had fallen in love with one of them during the time the soldiers had spent repairing their ship. He promised to marry her and take her to Rome with him. One morning she hurried down to the beach to tell him some wonderful, happy news. She was going to have his baby. When she arrived, the beach was empty. The ship had sailed at dawn and he had gone without her. He never returned.

She named her baby Flos, because it was the Roman word for flower. The more time passed, the more time her mother spent staring out to sea and the more wine she drank to dull her heartache. Flos collected and sold wild flowers to support them both. Mother may have been broken hearted, but Flos also suffered. Her suffering came from feelings of guilt. She often used to wonder why her father had gone and never came back. Flos thought that perhaps he did not want her. This made her feel unloved. She also thought that she must have been a bad child and that is why he did not come back for her now. Then Flos used to look at her mother in her half-drunk, heartbroken state and wonder if her mum blamed her for him not coming back. Perhaps he loved mum, but would not come back for her, because he did not want Flos. Flos used to lie on her straw bed at night thinking about these things until her head spun. Each night, her confusion and hurt saw Flos crying herself to sleep. Mum's abandonment by her lover hurt mum so deeply that she could not bring herself to talk to Flos about it. So, both suffered in silence and Flos never got the chance to realise that it was not her fault, but just something that happens between adults sometimes.

Eventually, her mother died. Whether it was from the alcohol, or a broken heart, or both, it was never known, but that is how Flos came into this world and that is how she became one of the many little lost souls that wandered the streets through no fault of their own.

Every night, Andromeda used to walk in the palace gardens and send the guards to fetch her shawl – on the excuse that she was cold. As soon as they had gone, she would let Flos into the gardens through a small door in the wall and Flos would sleep in the summerhouse where Andromeda left her food. If the queen had ever found out, she would have gone berserk and the guards would certainly have been beheaded for allowing such a breach of security.

There are many stories about Andromeda's kindness, but there is one particular event that just has to be told, because it was really spooky.

This is what happened:

One day Andromeda packed a picnic, gave her guards the slip and went off to walk along the beach. She needed to be alone, because she had to sort out some very confusing feelings she had been having recently about a young king named Perseus. Let's not beat about the bush. Actually, she was in love with him, but didn't know it yet.

Having slipped her guards, Andromeda was daydreaming along the beach when she heard a cry for help. She could see a bundle of black clothing bobbing about on the ocean, then realised it was an old woman who was apparently drowning. Andromeda dived in the rough sea and dragged her to the safety of the shore. The old woman said that she had been picking cockles on the rocks and fell into the water. Andromeda made a fire and shared her picnic with the old crone whilst their clothes dried. Eventually, the elderly lady donned her dried-out clothes and said she must go, but before she left she gave Andromeda a gold ring in gratitude. Andromeda had tried to refuse the gift. She had saved the woman's life and that was reward enough.

The old lady insisted on giving her the ring. Her reasons were that she had no relatives in this world to leave it to and it would not be long before she would be leaving this life anyway. What the woman was telling Andromeda was true, but it was not quite the truth as Andromeda understood it to be. The old hag was telling a different kind of truth. The aged woman had no relatives in this world, because she was Athena. The reason it would not be long before she left this life was because she was about to transform back to a goddess and return to the heavens.

It transpires that Athena had come to an agreement with Zeus that he would remove her blemishes if she fulfilled certain conditions. The terms were that she would have to go down to Earth in human form and 'rough it for a while'. Zeus hoped that it would teach Athena the attribute of humility. The only way she would be able to attain release from her Earthly existence would be to find another human being to do her a kindness. On top of that, she would have to prove to Zeus that she had learned the attribute of consideration towards others by returning that kindness. Zeus had decreed that Athena was to go to Earth in the guise of an old woman, because he knew it would make life difficult for her. How right he was!

It was a greedy society in the city of Queen Cassiopeia, where looks, image, money and possessions were everything. Personality and a decent character were not valued much. Being an old woman and 'past her sell-by date' put Athena out of the running for looks and cool image, so she was cut dead from the social scene. She was also looked down upon, because of her poverty. Nobody wanted to get involved with the poor old soul in case they got lumbered with having to look after her. That would have caused them personal inconvenience and worse still – it could cost them money, which they needed for themselves for dining out and the latest clothes. So, when Athena begged for food on the street corners, people laughed at her or kicked her aside.

What Athena really found annoying was that her old age had given her partial deafness and she often required people to repeat themselves when they deemed to speak to her. 'Hearing' people rarely gave thought to, or made allowances for, the affliction of deafness and the 'hard of hearing'. So, as was the case with the people that Athena came across, they never for one moment considered the possibility that she might be deaf. Instead they always assumed that she was a bit stupid, because she was slow at taking things in. Consequently, most of them ignored her altogether. After all, what could an 'old wrinkly' who has 'lost it' have to say that was interesting to them? If only they had bothered to make the effort, that old woman could have given them knowledge and experience beyond their wildest dreams!

It was a great relief to Athena when she finally came across Andromeda. Athena really did give the gold ring to her in genuine gratitude. Andromeda finally accepted the ring for fear of offending the old woman. As she slipped it on her finger, Andromeda saw that it had an electric-blue coloured 'A' engraved on it and a mysterious pattern marked out in diamonds.

When Andromeda asked what the pattern was, the old woman replied:

"It is your destiny."

Andromeda looked up to ask her what she meant by that, but the old woman had vanished. All that remained was the pile of black rags on the wet sand and not one footprint leading anywhere.

The two foregoing stories of Andromeda's kindness to Flos and the old woman serve to demonstrate why the common people adored her. However, in the case of the young Perseus, it was more than just adoration. Perseus was the King of Mycenae. He stood well over two metres tall, was of muscular physique with wide shoulders and neck like a bull. He had thick, tightly curled black hair and a full bearded angular face with steely blue eyes. He was what one might describe as handsome – 'in a rugged sort of way'.

Perseus was deeply in love with Andromeda. Of course, he appreciated her beauty – as all her suitors did, but it was more than just that. Yes, she was adept at carrying out her royal duties when visiting kings came to court – of which Perseus was just one of many. Yes, she was highly intelligent, well educated, good mannered and an absolute stunner in her Arachne spun dresses. Above all those things though, Perseus loved her for the same reasons that the common people loved her. It was her kindness towards others less fortunate than herself. She was the woman that he wanted for his wife and a woman that his people would want for their queen.

Perseus was kind to his people, a courageous warrior, honourable, trustworthy and the sort that would not betray a lady. These were the qualities that equally attracted Andromeda to him. They secretly started to meet as often as they could in the gardens of the palace. One star-strewn night, he asked her to marry him and become his queen. She readily accepted. Being a man of honour, he said he would go to her mother, Queen Cassiopeia, and ask her permission for Andromeda's hand in marriage.

Neither Andromeda, nor Perseus were selfish people and it was agreed that their needs would have to wait until he had first completed a vital task. It seems that a small fishing community, just outside his kingdom, had been attacked by a horde of bandits whilst the fishermen were at sea. The women and children had been carried off into slavery. Their king, who was a drunkard and a coward, had done nothing to stop it. They appealed to Perseus for help. Being a man with a sense of duty and justice, he had agreed to take his army that very night to set out and rescue them. Before he left, Perseus swore on his honour that he would never ever desert Andromeda.

Chapter 8

A Bit of a Beastly Problem

It was whilst Perseus was away that the trouble started for Andromeda. Some snivelling snitch of a servant girl had overheard their conversation in the palace gardens and reported it to Queen Cassiopeia. The queen went in a rage. "A princess of such beauty as my daughter could get herself someone much better than him", she stormed. Actually, no one could find anyone better than Perseus, because he was such an honourable man. That did not mean anything to Cassiopeia, because what she was talking about was cash – not character. There was a king in a neighbouring country that had more gold than the rest of the other kingdoms put together and she intended to marry her daughter off to him.

In her rage, Cassiopeia shouted: "My daughter is not going to marry any second rate king. She will marry the richest one."

Then she really put her foot in it, because she ranted to the heavens above: "Andromeda's beauty is greater than the Nereids – if not Hera herself!"

The Nereids were *Sea Nymphs* and known to ride around on sea horses, sometimes in the form of lovely human maidens and other times, part maiden with the tail of a fish. When they heard Queen Cassiopeia's wild claim, they were deeply insulted at the hurt caused to their pride. This was a problem in itself, but there was a greater problem than that. Whilst Zeus was *King of the Heavens*, he also had a brother named Poseidon and Poseidon was *King of the Oceans*. The Nereids were Poseidon's personal attendants! The sea nymphs went sniffling to their master and he shook with anger. If his attendants had been insulted then *he* had been insulted! In his temper Poseidon called forth a sea monster, named Cetus, from beneath the ocean bed. Cetus was the size of a mountain and Poseidon sent it to wreak havoc on the city of Queen Cassiopeia.

The first citizens to become aware of the monster's arrival were the fishermen out at sea. Their boats began to rock violently from side to side as the water began to boil and bubble. Then Cetus burst out from the depths. Some sailors screamed at the terrible sight of the beast, whilst others screamed because they had seen a different horror. The sailors that had been looking out to sea were the ones who saw a black slimy head, the size of a house, appear out of the water. Saucer-shaped eyes, glowing like red-hot coals, stared down at them. Below the eyes was a hooked nose with stinking green seaweed hanging from the nostrils. A corkscrew-shaped horn twisted out from the centre of its forehead. When Cetus opened his mouth, the men saw the terrifying sight of rows of gleaming white teeth. The thick, yellow gobs of saliva that dripped from the monster's blue, blubbery lips were licked and flicked by a darting forked tongue. The monster gave out a howl so loud that it ripped the sails off the boats and made the eardrums of the sailor's bleed.

For the sailors that had been looking over the sides of their boats at the bubbling water below, the sight was just as horrific. At the same moment as Cetus rose out of the sea to his full towering height, the surrounding water was drawn upwards with the monster's enormous body. Those looking over the sides saw the water beneath their boats dropping like a stone to the seabed below. As if in slow-motion, the ships seemed to hang in mid-air for eternity then start to plummet down the empty spiralling tunnel of death to the sea's sandy bottom. The broken bodies of those sailors that had not been killed with the impact could only lay amongst the splintered boats and stare up in terror at the thundering walls of water as the tunnel started to collapse on top of them.

Then Cetus trudged out of the ocean, up the beach and into the city. The beast's armour-plated tail whipped from side to side, knocking down houses and sweeping up people fleeing along the streets. Their bodies were tossed through the air and smashed to pulp against the city walls.

Queen Cassiopeia sent an army of three thousand men out of the palace to drive the beast back into the sea. The soldiers could only hack at its ankles then gaze in disbelief at their buckled swords. The archers fired hundreds of arrows towards its heart, but they just bounced off the monster's chest. When the army realised they were helpless against it, they panicked and started to run. It was too late. Cetus stamped down amongst them. His webbed feet crushed fifty soldiers at a time. The shovel-like hands of the sea monster scooped up hundreds of men, women and children and stuffed them into its slobbering jaws. Even the screams of those being cut in half by the razor sharp teeth did not hide the cracking sound of splintering bones.

Of the three thousand strong army, only two hundred soldiers survived. They dragged themselves back to the palace in utter shock and disarray.

The monster, having satisfied its hunger, returned to the sea. Only the vibrations in the ground from the footsteps of Cetus could be felt and the odd distant scream heard from those still half alive that were skewered on the beast's horn.

That evening, a sea sprite appeared at the court of the palace. It was only a small, blue, spindly creature, but the courtiers fell to their knees in terror, because they knew it was a messenger from Poseidon.

The sprite pointed at Cassiopeia and said:

"My master demands a sacrifice to restore the honour of his attendants, the Nereids. You have seven days to prepare. On the seventh day, the offering will be chained to a rock out at sea for sacrifice to the monster, Cetus. If you fail to do this, the beast will be sent to destroy your city and slaughter every inhabitant."

Cassiopeia slumped back on her throne with relief. 'This will be easy' she thought. 'I just have to buy it off with gifts.'

"What is it that Poseidon demands?" she huffed. "A pile of gold? A thousand casks of wine? A thousand bushels of wheat, or all those things?"

The sprite raised a stick-like arm with a pointing twig-like finger. Slowly the pointing finger moved around the court. Then it stopped.

"My master" said the thin reedy voice, "Demands that!"

There was a hush as the courtiers stood motionless with their eyes tight shut – praying to Zeus that it was not pointing at them. Slowly, they opened their eyes to stare at the finger. Then a sigh of relief from the courtiers, ministers and all the other royal 'hangers-on', wafted around the walls of the palace. The finger was not pointing at them. It was pointing at Andromeda!

The sea sprite vanished, leaving the courtiers twiddling with their fingers, or staring at the floor. No one could bring themselves to look at Andromeda.

Queen Cassiopeia sent for all her political advisors and military personnel to come up with a solution to this nightmare. They shut themselves in the banquet hall all night to argue ideas and devise plans that might overcome the beast. When dawn came, they returned to the court to announce their conclusions. A hush came over the murmuring crowd as the top military leader bowed before the queen. He announced that it had been concluded that it was impossible to stop the monster. To try to do so would lead to the complete destruction of the city and slaughter of the population. More important to them than that, it could endanger the lives of the queen herself and all the other nobles and government ministers.

"Therefore", he continued in a grave voice, "It is advised that the queen gives her approval for the sacrifice of Andromeda as demanded."

This was followed by utter silence from the Lords and Ladies gathered there. No one came forward in Andromeda's defence, because they were all too concerned for their own safety.

The queen rose from her throne without even glancing at the shaking Andromeda. Looking down at the marble floor, Cassiopeia avoided contact with her daughter's eyes then left the court. Andromeda, encircled by the onlookers, stood utterly alone. The queen's actions were taken as a sign of approval of her Government's advice and the palace guards, under orders of the Generals, moved in on her.

Andromeda was locked in a room at the top of the palace tower. This had been stocked with every personal comfort to aid her preparation for death. However, perfume, wines and jewellery mean nothing when you are alone without friendship and waiting to die a horrible death. Yet, not one person in the palace came to visit her. Their consciences were too riddled with guilt at what they were doing to this innocent young princess.

Chapter 9

The Marathon of Flos

Andromeda, now alone in the world, wept. She wept for herself then, moving to the window, she looked out across the green plains and the brown hills to the horizon beyond and wept for Perseus. Through the hot thermals of air that spiralled up to stifle the lofty room that was her prison, a little voice rose up from the ground. Andromeda looked down to the courtyard far below and saw the tiny figure of Flos. Flos was waving, but it could be seen that her waif-like body was shaking with fear. Andromeda could not hear the words shouted by Flos, but guessed she was calling out her sorrow.

Andromeda looked at the ring on her finger that the old woman had given to her. She remembered that the woman gave it because she knew she was not long for this world and it was of no use to her anymore. Andromeda once more studied the mysterious pattern of sparkling diamonds on the ring. Was her coming sacrifice the destiny that the old woman had spoken of? Whatever it meant, it did not matter now. Andromeda also knew that she was not long for this world and the ring was of no more use to her now than it had been to the old woman. 'Perhaps Flos could sell it and make a better life for herself' she thought. Carefully, she slipped it off her finger and dropped it to the distant ground. She saw the arms of Flos go up and a last flash of the diamonds in the sunshine as the ring disappeared into her hands.

"Got it!" squealed Flos triumphantly. Then she turned and ran like a startled rabbit, neither pausing to wave goodbye, nor turning to take a last look back. 'Perhaps she has seen a guard coming' thought Andromeda as she watched Flos climb a grapevine up the palace wall, throw herself over the top and disappear.

Flos had not seen a guard coming. She had another urgent thought on her mind. The rotten snitch of a servant girl had not been the only one in the palace gardens the night Perseus had proposed marriage to Andromeda. Flos had been there too. She had also heard Perseus say where he was going to give battle against the bandits. Now she needed to get there at all costs to tell him what had happened. He, alone, was the only one that could save her beloved Andromeda. Andromeda had been a friend, a sister and a mother to Flos and she was not going to let her down in her hour of need. Ahead of her lay high hills, steep valleys, fast flowing rivers, rock-strewn plains and four sun-scorched days and bitter-cold nights of tortuous travel. Flos slipped Andromeda's ring on her finger. She would need to produce the ring to prove to Perseus that her plea of help for Andromeda was genuine. Flos gritted her teeth and set off to run her own personal Marathon. It was to be a race of endurance against time and injustice that any ancient Greek athlete would have been proud to literally run himself to death for.

Flos ran the rock-strewn plains and the blood oozed from her feet as the stones cut into her soles. She dragged herself up the hills and their slopes seemed to clad her legs with lead as she forced one foot in front of the other. The depth of the valleys took their toll as their steepness dragged her tired body forwards, so that she fell and tumbled head over heels time and again. Shreds of hair were ripped from her scalp and her arms and legs were slashed in crazy zigzag patterns by thorn bushes as she drove herself through the thick clinging forests. During the day, the sun beat down on her blistered lips and dry, puffy eyes. At night, the cold shook the flesh on her frozen, aching bones, but she still cried aloud her gratitude to Artemis, *Goddess of the Moon* for shining brightly and lighting her way. She did not stop to eat or drink, but grasped at berries as she lunged through the bushes and bent to scoop water to her cracked lips as she waded through the dragging rivers.

As the sun's blood-red knives sliced open the dawning of the fourth morning, Flos staggered into a clearing in the depths of a dense wood. She suddenly stood still. Her body rocked backwards and forwards from fatigue as she fought to focus her burning eyes on the sight in front of her. Through the haze of her spinning head, she saw two paths. One veered off to the left and one to the right. One would take her back inland with the prospect of needlessly wasted hours and the other would take her on to the coast where Perseus would be camped with his army. Which path though? She shook her head to try and clear her dazed mind and make the correct decision, but it just made her head throb even more. Her bone-dry throat rasped so loud with every breath she gulped down that she did not hear the movement ahead of her in the bushes. Nor did her tired eyes see another pair of eyes that were watching her! Flos hesitantly moved towards the right-hand path.

The watching eyes saw this and the face of the creature they belonged to winced with frustration. "Not that way you silly girl", mumbled the creature under its breath. "It's the left-hand path you want! Stupid girl's got no sense of direction", it moaned to itself. "Couldn't track an elephant in a snowdrift. Ah, well, I suppose I will have to do what I'm famous for, then she will go the correct way."

The creature was Pan, the *God of the Fields, Hills and Woods*. Shepherds, tenders of cattle and beehives and those that went hunting and fishing worshipped him. Pan looked after the countryside and all those people that used it. He loved music and often danced with the wood nymphs. It is said that he invented the panpipes so that he could dance with them. Pan was a short, human-looking creature, but he had two goat's horns growing out of his head, a goat's beard on his chin, pointed ears, a goat's tail and two hairy goat's legs that he walked upright upon.

Pan was also a bit of a prankster. Actually, a lot of people have met him at some time in their lives, but did not know it. They may have been walking down a street or country lane late at night, happy as a pig in muck, with not a soul about. Then suddenly, they could have sworn they saw something ahead in the distance, but were not quite sure. Perhaps they thought they heard a sound behind them, but no one was there. Or they became uneasy and had a feeling that there was someone watching. Their pulse quickens and they start to walk faster. Then the mind really starts working overtime and they panic and start to run. They get home safe and sound. Never saw a thing. Nothing happened and they wonder what all the fuss was about. Well, that was Pan! When he got bored, or some chattering travellers disturbed his slumbers, he would suddenly appear to them out of nowhere. Surprise would turn to fear. Then they would run faster than a cornered rat up a drainpipe. In other words (per the dictionary) they would panic:-

"From the Greek word *panikos* – of the god Pan – who had a reputation for causing panic."

It was puzzling at first as to what the little god Pan had got to do with Flos. Then it transpired that he often lazed in the long grass and watched her picking the wild flowers. He frowned upon her activity at first and had a mind to jump up and scare the living daylights out of her. However, he took the trouble to find out why she was doing this and realised it was to feed herself and her mother. What really made him forgive Flos and take an interest in her welfare was that she always kept some of the seeds and planted them ready for next spring. Actually, she spread more of the wild flower seeds about than the plants could normally do for themselves. She put back more than she took out. Now that was a human being Pan could warm to and that was the reason why he was taking an interest in her business. Pan was a god and therefore he knew why she was running her little heart out and where she was trying to reach.

Flos continued to move towards the right-hand path. "I don't like doing this, but there's nothing else for it", grumbled Pan. "I'll have to frighten her so she runs down the left path." He took a deep breath, raised himself up on his hind legs and went, "Booooooooooooo!" Flos screamed – panicked – and ran for all she was worth down the left path. Forgotten now were her aching legs and bleeding feet. She ran until she dropped from exhaustion. Pan knew that she had not far to go now to reach the camp of Perseus He let her have a short rest then he did his "Boooooooo!" act again and she dragged herself up and staggered off again in panic. This went on all the fourth day until dusk. Finally, Flos collapsed to the ground. Despite Pan's efforts, all the booing in the world did not move her this time – she was unconscious. In the twilight, Pan could see the glow from the army's campfires by the seashore – some fifteen kilometres away. There was nothing else for it. Pan picked up the limp body, slung Flos on his back and set off at a gallop.

Perseus and his army were resting. They had battled all afternoon against the bandits and finally won. Those bandits that had not been killed ran away. Those that had been taken prisoner were made to bury the dead. Perseus intended to take the prisoners to the king, whose realm it was, so that they could be put on trial and imprisoned. All the women and children had been safely rescued and Perseus saw to it that his men fed and made them comfortable. He moved amongst the women and talked to them of what had happened. It seems that the bandits had invaded another village with the intention of stealing all the wine. However, the inhabitants had heard they were coming and ran away into the hills. The grapes had not been harvested and therefore the wine had still not been made. The bandits had then abducted the fishing village women and children, dragged them to the wine-growing village and forced them to collect the grapes and make the wine.

Now, it was widely known that Perseus was a courageous warrior, but he was also a kind and tolerant man. It took a lot to make him angry, but what the women told him next sent him into such a rage that even his own soldiers drew back from him in fear. The women and the children had been slaving in the fields under the hot sun without being given any water. They were also beaten with sticks. That was terrible enough, but there was worse to follow. The bandit leader thought they were not working quickly enough for his liking, so he and four of his cronies took a child each and slit their throats to make the women work faster.

Perseus could live with most things that men do, but men that harmed women and children were not men in his eyes, they were not even human – they were evil monsters. He got the women to pick out the five men responsible, ordered his own soldiers to move away and then threw five swords at the feet of the bandits. Eyes blazing with rage, he stood in front of them and between gritted teeth hissed the words: "Now come and slit *my* throat." The bandits swept up the swords and charged at him together. Perseus twisted, ducked, weaved and sprang so fast that his whole body was like a spinning-top. All the time, his sword was a silver blur that seemed to hover on its own in mid air and rotate around his body. It was all over in minutes. Perseus stood alone in the middle of what appeared to be a circular red carpet. It was no carpet though. It was the sand that had been coloured crimson from the spurting blood of the bandits. Around his feet lay the headless, limbless bodies of the criminals. Their heads, arms and legs were scattered around the entire circumference of the oozing circle. Perseus roared to the heavens with anguish. In frustration at the death of the children he snapped the avenging sword across his knee threw it into the sea and walked away.

The camp was quiet as Pan drew near. The soldiers, women and children were all asleep. The only people awake were the camp guards and Perseus. He was sitting alone in a small cave at the foot of the cliffs. He had been brooding about the streaks of evil that ran through the veins of some people and why the gods allowed it. Then his thoughts turned to his gentle Andromeda. He loved her so much that his heart ached to be away from her.

lands. The queen did not take kindly to this public humiliation, particularly as her name happened to be Boudicca. She joined forces with other discontented people and went on the rampage with a formidable army, burning towns and heavily defeating sections of the Roman army that tried to stop her. One of the major Roman cities that she burned down was Camalodunum (or Colchester, as we know it now).

Cassius and Flos had heard that Boudicca was on the rampage and could come their way. So, they filled a chest with every Aureus (solid gold Roman coin) they possessed. The gold coins were the remains of the substantial fortune that Flos's father had given to her when he died, plus the money they had made from exporting crops off their farm to Rome. They loaded the chest onto a cart and took it off to a distant hill to bury it. When the danger was over, they intended to return and reclaim their fortune. Just in case the worst happened and they were killed, they left a manuscript inside the chest, which gave details of legal ownership. Having buried it, they set off to the neighbouring villa to tell their son, Paulus Cassius what they had done. However, on the way there, they were overtaken by a stray band of Boudicca's army and surrounded.

Cassius and Flos were now in the twilight of their life. Their love for each other ran deep and strong. It had been doubly strengthened as they struggled side by side to survive the tests that life sends along. Flos and Cassius had taken their vows of marriage in a temple at Rome and in their eyes and the eyes of the gods, was one inseparable spirit. They were determined that nothing would ever part them. They clasped hands and stood back to back. Cassius drew his sword, Flos drew her dagger and they fought for their own life and each others. Ten Britons were killed as they fell upon the couple and Flos only stopped fighting when she heard Cassius cry out and felt his hand go limp in hers as his body slumped behind her. She turned and saw him lying face-up with a spear in his chest. His hand was reaching up towards her. As the killer of her husband moved forward to lunge the spear deeper into his body, Flos lashed out with her dagger and slit his throat. She then placed the dagger in Cassius's outstretched hand and threw herself upon it. They died in each other's arms.

Eventually, the Roman governor-general of Britannia, Seutonias Paulinus, defeated Boudicca and she poisoned herself after the battle. Paulus Cassius buried his parents and then returned to his parent's villa. It had been completely burned down. He and his wife rebuilt it and they started again; for in the midst of death, life must go on.

Over the next three hundred years, the mixing, splitting and drifting apart of the descendants of Cassius and Flos continued. The Roman army had gradually started to pull out of Britannia by AD400 to defend Rome against attacks of barbarians from across the Rhine. This eventually left Britannia wide open to attack from others such as the Saxons, who settled in the south. Around AD800 the Vikings came over from Scandinavia and a lot settled in the north of England and created their own kingdoms. The descendants of Andromeda Flos, who upon marriage, had left her parents and moved up north with her Briton husband, became intermixed in marriage with those Vikings. The descendants of Paulus Cassius and his wife, who had stayed in The Midlands region of England to farm his parent's villa, became intermixed in marriage with the Saxons who had settled there.

Inevitably, the children of Flos and Cassius and their children and their children's children and so on and so forth, gradually became lost in the passing of time and history. The death of Medusa, her threat to the wild flowers and indeed, the very Earth itself, was also lost in the passing of time and history.

CHAPTER 15

THEY THINK IT'S ALL OVER

It would currently be excusable for Mother Nature's appointed guardians of her wild flowers – the White Archangels – to think it's all over. A couple of thousand years had now elapsed since Perseus killed Medusa. The evil wild flowers that she had planted around the hill of the golden Bluebell, near the village of Tevlingorde, budded each spring, blossomed every summer, then died away each autumn to sleep all winter. This had gone on for the last two thousand years and not a peep from them. They had awaited the return of Medusa and her command to attack, but it never came.

The White Archangels had kept an eye on the strange wild flowers planted amongst them from the start. However, nothing had ever happened and the silvery light of Electra's star still shone brightly down upon them from the Pleiades constellation. Electra had every right to be happy. She knew something that the White Archangels did not know – Medusa had got the chop and now the wild flowers of Earth were safe. The White Archangels were content that if Electra was happy and shining bright, then everything must be going nicely.

It did go nicely right up to the present day – until mankind put his foot in it. Well, not actually his foot – he put his drill in it. It is recorded in Greek mythology that Medusa had two other Gorgon sisters named Euryale and Stheno. Their mother was Ceto, who happened to be a sea monster. Medusa, being born in the form of a beautiful maiden, had spent most of her time on land. Her two sisters also had the ability to dwell on land, but coming from slightly 'fishy' backgrounds they also had a very odd habit. Every now and then they would disappear to a random cavern underneath the seabed and have a 'catnap' for the odd ten thousand years. Let's face it, they could do with all the beauty-sleep they could get. So, there was Stheno, snug as a bug underneath the North Sea, when some idiot floated along with his shiny new oilrig. He parked it smack over her bedroom and proceeded to drill down through the ceiling. Stheno did not take kindly to this and in a rage she snapped off the drill and sent it hurtling back up the hole faster than a bullet up a barrel. The Accident Investigation Team's report stated that the almighty explosion that destroyed the rig was due to a gas pressure blowback and it had been one of those unfortunate terrible accidents.

Now she was awake, Stheno decided she might as well return to Greece and visit her favourite sister, Medusa. 'Anyway' she thought, 'The old bag still owes me a couple of lipsticks that she borrowed'. Anxiously awaiting her arrival was 'miss muck stirrer of the millennium' – Hecate.

"Oh, it's awful darling," Hecate simpered gleefully. "You better sit down before I tell you what happened to that sweetykins sister of yours. No! Don't sit there you'll drip seaweed on the Persian Rug." Stheno slid over to the next chair and promptly sat on the sharp end of Hecate's pointed witch's hat. As the hat's point probed her haemorrhoids, she shot to the roof of the cave and hit her head on a black cat in the rafters – whose curiosity had previously turned it to stone. Stheno was not amused and gave Hecate a glare that would sink a battleship. In the interests of self-preservation, Hecate decided that she better get on with the story a bit smartish.

"It was that Perseus chappy who did it for the sake of that treacly, goody, goody, Andromeda wench. Big sword! Smack in the kisser! Head wanged off like a coconut at the fairground! Wonderfully bad luck and all that. And that Flos brat didn't help either – going off on her Sunday afternoon charity run to get ten brownie-points. Pity about Medusa's wild flower plan though. It was a cracker. Could have destroyed the world don't ya know?"

Stheno's ears immediately pricked up at that last bit of information and she showed great interest in its possibilities.

Stheno decided that she would finish the job for her sister and get total revenge on the human race. She would have a rest, make her plans and then fly to Britain and activate Medusa's evil wild flowers. Stheno would get the golden Bluebell whilst the Earth would get icy oblivion. The Gorgon sat and gazed into the boiling cauldron of Hecate's newly mixed 'Death Pudding' and pictured the death, misery and suffering to mankind that was soon to come. At the very same moment that Stheno was daydreaming about forthcoming death, misery and suffering in her cave in Greece – death, misery and suffering were already inflicting themselves upon the teenagers, Poppy and her twin brother St John, in a city in northern England.

CHAPTER 16

POPPY AND St JOHN

It was a warm July morning, but the sky was dull and overcast. The smudgy grey clouds hung low and heavy as they drizzled their contents onto the muddy grass upon which Poppy and St John were standing. St John – of stocky build, angular features, with blue eyes and tousled fair hair - stared, unseeing, across at his father. Poppy – of slender build, pale heart-shaped face, with soft brown eyes and long black hair – was, as if in a trance. She watched in morbid curiosity at the small swaying movements near her feet. Everything around them seemed to be a blur through the heavy drizzle and the tears that welled in their eyes. The vicar's softly spoken words; "Dust to dust, ashes to ashes," threaded their way through the whispering hiss of the rain and crept into Poppy's wandering thoughts. The words hit her like a sledgehammer and her mind was wrenched back to the here and now.

The small, swaying movements near Poppy's feet, which she barely saw in her trance, came starkly into focus. It was the coffin slowly being lowered into the ground. The sun reluctantly peeked through the clouds for a brief moment and the raindrops split its light into a rainbow overhead. The colours illuminated the brass nameplate on the lid, which read: 'Rose Flos Hayward'. Poppy sank to her knees beside the grave and sobbed: "Mum! Mum!" into the black recess of her mother's final resting-place. The few friends of the family that had attended the funeral now silently drifted away to leave Poppy Flos Hayward and her twin brother, St John Cassius Hayward, to be alone with their thoughts.

As the two young people and their father stood quietly in their own personal world of memories, Poppy looked down at the gold ring that she self-consciously twisted back and forth on her finger in anxiety. Despite the dullness of the day, the electric-blue coloured 'A' engraved on the ring and the mysterious pattern of diamonds still glittered against the shining background of gold. Her mother had said that it had been with the female line of the family for generations, just as the middle names Flos had for the girls and Cassius had for the boys. The names and the ring had originated from that far back in the distant past that no one could remember why they were carried. It was thought to be just a family tradition. Her mother had promised the ring to Poppy when she died. It was the only gift that Poppy Flos Hayward had dreaded receiving. Poppy looked up from the ring and across the grave to her dad. Once again, her gaze was misted over by the veil of remembrance and Poppy's thoughts dreamily slipped back into fleeting cameos that pictured their life as a family.

Poppy remembered how her mum and dad had been when they were together. No matter what they had never had in their lives, her parents had made up for it by having each other and the unshakeable love between them. Dad had a low paid job in a factory and had been made redundant several times, but they got by. Mum used to do part-time cleaning jobs at a supermarket and a bank on the sprawling council estate where the family lived. She would get up at 5 am to clean at the bank and go to do the supermarket late at night. The money she earned bought little 'extras' for the family.

Some of the money went towards paying for sword fencing lessons for St John. It was something he had wanted to do, because he had always felt deep inside that he would be good at it. Mum had encouraged him from the first time he showed an interest. The fencing master had said that St John was a 'natural' and mum used to say that it must be in his ancestral blood. The kids on the estate used to make fun of him and said it was for 'snobs' and 'nancies', but the fencing master had told him that if he kept working hard at it, one day he would be representing his country. He was already representing his county.

St John was not exactly the flavour of the month with most of the kids on the estate anyway, because he wasn't 'with-it'. Whilst they were hanging around the shops and street corners in the evening – discussing really important issues about which pop song would top the charts next week, or which film star was having whose baby – he would be out in the back garden looking up at the heavens. This came about as a result of his dad buying him two things from a second hand shop that had started St John off on his other interest – namely, a battered pair of binoculars and a dog-eared book on astronomy by the astronomer, Professor Paul Poultney. The facts and descriptions that Paul Poultney wrote about the stars fascinated St John, but to actually be able to see and identify some of them with the binoculars made it doubly exciting. The vastness of it all made him feel so small. Yet having knowledge about how stars were created and how they functioned, gave him a tremendous sense of fulfilment.

He was soon able to recognise different constellation star patterns and name them. Their names also gripped his imagination and he soon realised that most of them were named after gods and divine creatures from ancient myth. Consequently, it was not long before he had saved his pocket-money, tramped around the second-hand book shops and bought a book on the gods and goddesses of Greek and Roman mythology to find out who they were and what they had done. Then he wanted to know more about the ancient peoples who had lived under the rule of those gods. Once he started learning about these things, he wanted more and more.

As she stood at her mother's graveside, Poppy's reminiscences then drifted to the unhappy time she and her brother were suffering at the community college on the estate where they lived. They had both been subjected to bullying and verbal torment ever since they had moved up from primary school. The bullies had plenty of ammunition to fire at them – their names for starters! Mum had named them both after wild flower*s*. Poppy wasn't so bad for a girl and she could cope with that, but St John had problems from the other kids about his name. Mum had named him after the wild flower – St John's Wort. He kept telling everybody that his name was pronounced 'Sinjun', but they still insisted on sneeringly calling him Saint John and 'Holy Joe', etc. Both of them kept it quiet about their middle names of Flos and Cassius. Who could blame them? What made it worse were their birthmarks, which the other kids constantly ridiculed. Poppy had a large yellow blotch on the back of her right hand in the shape of a Bluebell and St John had a white blotch on the back of his right hand in the shape of a star. Mum tried to make them feel better about it by passing them off as the 'marks of destiny'. The twins never believed it, but they were always grateful for the loving efforts of their comforting mother.

A few really horrible kids put it around that the birthmarks were 'The marks of the devil'. There was a group of girls that used to chant: "Witch, witch!" every time Poppy walked by – an echo of ignorance from the distant past? They were led by a girl with a big mouth, named Lin. Under her breath, Poppy used to call her 'Big Gob-Lin and her Pixies'. It made her smile to herself, but it did not make up for the hurt of being called a witch all the time or being pushed around in the school corridors. St John did not do a lot better with the bullyboys. Whilst some would poke him in the chest and chant: "Devil, devil" in his face, some would come up behind and put two fingers above his head in the shape of mock devil's horns.

The worst and most hurtful abuses were when they were both called 'The loony witch's kids'. That was a direct insult to their mother. St John could tolerate a lot of things, but could not stand anything hurtful against his mum. She was a kind, sensitive person who loved and cared for Poppy, St John and their dad. There is nothing she would not do for them in her love. 'Perhaps some of the bully kids were jealous, because they didn't have it themselves' thought St John. He sometimes got into fights about it and ended up being sent to 'Time-out'. It was pointless trying to explain to the teachers what the fights were about. "How could I?" he used to say to Poppy. "They wouldn't understand. It would just make it worse."

What St John had meant was that mum had a love for flowers – particularly wild flowers, with which she had a special gift. Whenever dad was at work and the kids were on holiday, she would pack up a picnic and they would catch a bus into the countryside to study and admire the wild flowers. If any of the flowers seemed to her not to be thriving, she would take them home and nurture them back to health. Often, she would keep the wild flowers until they had seeded and then plant the seedlings back in the wild, so that she put back more than she took out. She seemed to be able to do what she liked with them and they always grew for her.

A lot of times, she talked to her wild flowers. "It encourages them to grow stronger and sometimes, I swear I can hear little whispers coming back from them" she used to say to Poppy. Mum had also taught Poppy everything she knew about caring for and rearing wild flowers. Poppy knew the names of every one and, to her amazement, found that those that she praised and gave words of encouragement to also grew quicker and stronger for her as well. Mum had told Poppy that, she too, must also have the gift. However, Poppy never heard the flowers whispering back to her and always thought that mum was 'having her on' about that bit. Needless to say, mum was often overheard talking to her wild flowers in the garden and it soon got round the estate that she was 'a bit loony'. The fact that she used to disappear off into the woods and fields of the surrounding countryside led to speculation from the gossiping ignorant that she was performing some sort of black magic rituals out there. Hence came the insults to Poppy and St. John about being the 'Loony witch's kids'.

As Poppy wavered at the graveside in distant memories, her flash-backs now brought her closer to the present – to the scene at school where they had been taken from the classroom by the Principal. Their exit had been accompanied by sneering sounds from classmates who gleefully assumed that they were both in trouble. They had been led to the reception area where they saw dad sitting with grim mouth and white face. The fifteen-minute walk home seemed an eternity. Dad looked straight ahead and said nothing. Neither did the twins. They knew something was terribly wrong, but dare not ask what, because they dreaded to hear the answer. As soon as dad got them safely in home and away from prying eyes, he went on his knees, flung his arms around both, burst into tears and told them that mum was dead. Poppy had sunk to her knees with her arms around her father, her body racked with sobbing. St John stood motionless. He was gritting his teeth and trying not to cry, but his stomach was knotting and churning. He spluttered and coughed for a few seconds then flew out the back door and was sick down the drain.

An inquest was later held. It was reported to the Coroner's Court by the police that she was found at the bottom of a quarry on the outskirts of the city. From their enquiries with the family, it was a place that she had frequented on a number of occasions. It was concluded that she had accidentally fallen, resulting in death from a broken neck. A verdict of 'Death by misadventure' was recorded.

The presence of dad's arm, now gently hugging her shoulder, slowly brought Poppy's thoughts back to the present. "Come on Poppy," her father said quietly, "Let's go home." Poppy brushed the rain-soaked long black hair from her face and the tears from her eyes. All three huddled together and slowly walked back through the churchyard. St John took one last look back. The grave of his mother was slowly fading into the distance behind a grey swirling curtain of mist that seemed to be drawing itself around his mum's final resting place. For a split second he could have sworn he saw a goat-like figure standing upright in the midst of the swirling murk. He blinked and flicked his head to shake the rain out of his eyes. He stared again, but there was nothing. He opened his mouth, as if to say something to the others, but fell silent. After all, it had been a long day. His body ached with stress and his eyes were sore from having no sleep the night before. He mentally ticked himself off for being silly and huddled himself closer to his dad as they made their way home.

Although a finding of 'Death by misadventure' had been recorded, it was already starting to go around the estate that Rose Flos Hayward talked to flowers – so she was 'a bit loony'. The consequent conclusion of the ignorant was that she had obviously thrown herself off the top of the old limestone quarry and committed suicide in her mentally unstable state. No one would ever know – not even her family – that she was trying to save a Bee Orchid.

Bee Orchids are clever little wild flowers, because over thousands of years they have cunningly evolved the lower lip of each flower to look like the rear end of a bee. This gives the appearance that the imitation bee is crawling into the wild flower to look for nectar, which tempts real bees to do the same. Bee Orchids flower between June and July and grow in grassy places on chalk and limestone. This one had certainly found the right place to grow at an old limestone quarry, but it had not been so clever with the grassy place it had picked to grow on. Its clod of earth had slipped over the edge of the quarry with the heavy rain and was now balanced precariously on a ledge a few feet down the sheer rock face. Rose was stretching down to rescue it when suddenly, the ground crumbled away... and she was gone!

As they made their way home, Poppy thought about the suicide rumour and wondered how some people could be so vicious. They could not possibly know mum. She loved her family too much to ever, ever, want to leave them. 'Still, at least it's the start of the school summer holidays now' she thought to herself, 'So St John and I won't have to worry about facing those ugly taunts at school for a couple of months. The present is enough to cope with at the moment. It's no use worrying about that now and taking a dim view of the future'.

CHAPTER 17

A DIM VIEW OF THE FUTURE

Poppy was trying not to take a dim view of the future down on Earth, but Electra had definitely taken a dim view of the future up in the Pleiades. It was her wish that had brought about the beautiful wild flower garden in the universe that was Earth. Now she had seen a vision of what Stheno planned to do. However, she was helpless – placed far away as she was in the Pleiades constellation. All she could do was weep with anxiety at what was going to befall her beloved planet. The glitter of her starlight grew dimmer and dimmer.

Down on Earth, the White Archangel wild flowers had always looked up to the heavens to seek the reassurance of Electra's twinkling starlight. Now they saw it had dimmed to a glimmer and were also taking a dim view of the future. It was obvious that something was terribly wrong. They must be in danger. It had to be connected with the strange wild flowers that were still growing silently around the golden Bluebell on Honeypot Hill, near the village of Tevlingorde. What the threat was, they did not know, but they knew they needed help!

From the wild flowers' network of gossip that operated up and down the countryside the White Archangels were aware of a young girl up north who had a hidden gift with wild flowers and her twin brother who had knowledge of the gods and the stars. Local gossip, supplied by the Evening Primrose wild flowers that grew in Tevlingorde village, informed them that the two young people had a distant relative who lived in the village. She was a lady whom Poppy and St John knew as Aunt Kay – although they had never met her. Every birthday, she would send them a card and a little gift and they would write 'thank you' letters and send her a Christmas card. The White Archangels simply had to get the two of them to come down to Tevlingorde, stay with Aunt Kay and their help could be enlisted. Easier said than done.

Between them, the White Archangels proposed numerous complicated plans, but each one was greeted with jeers of: "Rhubarb, rhubarb!" from the Monk's Rhubarb wild flowers; Shouts of: "Load of bull!" from the Bulrushes and despairing jibes of: "Poppycock, utter poppycock!" from the Poppies. The wild flower, named Solomon's Seal, because it reckoned it was the wisest flower on the hill, came up with a brilliant, but simple solution:

"All we do is poison their old man see? Then there is no one to look after the kids. They don't know of any other relatives they've got, so they will have to come and stop with this Aunt Kay."

One of the White Archangels coughed politely and gently pointed out that they did not wish to become a bunch of murderers.

"No. I'm just joking," groaned Solomon's Seal. "We just poison him enough to put him in hospital for a couple of weeks. The Corn Marigolds that grow in the kids' back garden have told us that they see their old man have mushrooms every Sunday morning for his breakfast and that the kids don't like them – they have corn flakes. So, we recruit some mildly poisonous 'thicko' of a toadstool to hop in his breakfast mushrooms and do the bizzo."

"Yes. Very cunning," said another White Archangel. "But who would volunteer to be eaten?"

"No problem," Solomon's Seal said reassuringly. "These toadstools have big heads, but they've got no brains see? I know a cute, sweet-talking Bluebell up there. She will give one of the Toadstools the gooey-eyes treatment, feed him the hero bit about sacrificing his life for the good of mankind and that he will be reborn as a shining white mushroom to have eternal life in the great manure bed in the sky. After that, the 'thicko' will do anything."

Everyone agreed that it was the best plan – 'A toadstool a day keeps the Gorgons away' so to speak.

Sure enough, the following Sunday, to the simpering sounds of undying admiration from the sweet-talking Bluebell and rapturous applause from the back garden Corn Marigolds, a lone Toadstool stood on the kitchen windowsill above the cooker. He turned and dramatically addressed his audience:

"Remember me. 'Tis a far, far better thing I do now. Once more to the beach dear friends. The wings and sparrows of outrageous fortune. A cow, a cow, my kingdom for a cow."

It was common knowledge amongst the gathered wild flowers that the Toadstool had grown up on a lawn at the back of a library, but it had not apparently done much for his literary knowledge.

"Get on with it, fungus face!" yelled a Dwarf Thistle.

"For goodness sake! Somebody push him in," jeered a Cowslip.

The Toadstool turned, prayed to Mother Nature then jumped into the sizzling frying pan.

St John called the doctor out that evening. Dad was taken off to hospital with severe food poisoning. He had already spoken to Aunt Kay on the telephone – in between bouts of being sick in a bowl. It was arranged that his children would stay with her until he was well again.

CHAPTER 18

THE JOURNEY TO TEVLINGORDE

The following morning saw Poppy and St John walking down the platform at the railway station for the train that would take them south to the Midlands. On a grass embankment at the end of the platform, a Hedge Bindweed and a Field Pansy wild flower watched them sauntering along. Both teenagers struggled with suitcases that had been hurriedly stuffed with jeans, sweatshirts and spare trainers. Poppy was hoping to see some flower species that she had not seen before, growing in the area of her new temporary home. She clutched the precious possession of her mother's own notebooks and wild flower sketches close to her chest. St John had his old binoculars slung around his neck and his battered book on astronomy by Professor Paul Poultney tucked under his arm. He was hoping that he would see the stars much clearer in the countryside, away from the air and light pollution of the big city.

"Here they come," said the Field Pansy.

The Hedge Bindweed looked gob-smacked and blurted out: "You've got to be joking. Pull the other root – it's got bells on!"

"I'm not daft you know," squeaked the Field Pansy. "Look at the birthmarks on their hands. It is the sign. I know these things."

"Yes," sneered the Hedge Bindweed, "But look at them! They're just a couple of ankle-biters. What are they going to do – save us with a water pistol?"

"Hush," hissed the Field Pansy. "Poppy will hear you. Anyway, I am more worried about their father in hospital with Toadstool poisoning."

"Oh! Stop twittering on, ya great pansy," tutted the Hedge Bindweed. "The chances of him dying from that are about as rare as finding rocking-horse manure."

St John shuffled about uneasily on the platform as the train pulled in. "I am worried about dad," he confessed.

"Don't worry," muttered Poppy. "The chances of him dying from that are about as rare as finding rocking-horse manure."

St John burst out laughing. "Wherever did you get that from?"

Poppy gave him a puzzled look. "I don't know. It just sort of popped into my head."

They both jumped on the train and fought for a window seat. At Derby, they had to change trains for one that would take them to Leicester and on to Market Harborough where their Aunt Kay would be waiting for them.

"Goodness knows which platform we are supposed to go to now," said St John in a worried voice.

"Platform number three, you duffer!" screamed a clump of Ragwort wild flowers that were trespassing in a tub of Tulips on platform one.

"Platform number three, you duffer," mumbled Poppy.

"Oh! Yes," said St John shirtily. "I suppose that just popped in your head as well did it? Well, I'm going to ask the porter." He returned two minutes later. "Okay, know-all. Get your bag. We're going to platform three." He strode off haughtily in front of Poppy, who was still trying to work out how she knew it was platform three they wanted.

The train sped smoothly along. St John was flicking through his astronomy book. Poppy watched out of the window at the passing countryside. As their carriage whizzed past, an excited murmur rippled through the wild flowers that grew alongside the railway track. The words: "They are coming! They are coming!"

shot ahead of the train all the way to the White Archangels on Honeypot Hill.

It was a bright summer's day. The sky was Cornflower blue with little white puffballs of cloud dotted across it. The colour of the land criss-crossed back and forth from the gold of wheat fields to the rippling green of meadowland. A lonely scarecrow stood in one field with its arms outstretched as if it was pleading for someone to run up and give it a big hug. Poppy wondered if, in its loneliness, it was crying inside like she was now. She missed her mother. If mum had been with them now she would have been pointing out all sorts of things through the train window:

'Look at that Elm tree,' she would be saying. 'See how the shape of its crown is different from those Chestnuts?'

A train flashed by Poppy's window in the opposite direction and the rural scene flickered off and on like a failing light bulb. Then the last carriage of the invading train whipped past and there, on the horizon, Poppy spotted a Yew tree.

The Yew tree brought thoughts of her mother back to Poppy's mind again. Mum had always loved history and had a knack of bringing it to life for her children. If mum had been with them now, thought Poppy, she would have been saying:

'See that Yew tree? Their leaves are such a dark green colour that they look almost black. You can pick them out a mile away on the horizon. That's why, in olden times, people sometimes buried their treasure under them because Yews were easy to identify on the horizon and trace their way back to.'

'Yes,' smiled Poppy to herself, 'Mum had certainly known her trees and even how useful they had been to famous people throughout history.'

Poppy remembered how they had once come across a Yew tree whilst out on a picnic. Mum had related some interesting historical facts about the Yews. For instance, she had pointed out that some Yew trees were centuries old. Also, Yew wood is really springy and so strong that it was used in mediaeval times to make the famous English Long Bow.

Mum had told them that, because of the Long Bow, you could say that the Yew tree had helped save the life of King Henry V of England. She had explained that in the year AD1415 King Henry V of England had led an army of archers, foot soldiers and knights to France to lay claim to lands that he said belonged to him. After long sieges and many battles, he took possession of what he said was his by inheritance. He then left a garrison of men there and set out with the remainder of his small band of soldiers to return home to England.

However, on the way back to Calais his way was blocked near the village of Agincourt by a twenty thousand strong French army that heavily outnumbered his five thousand hungry, battle-weary and sick men. Henry obviously wanted to avoid a battle and tried to skirt round them, but the French, thinking victory would be easy, would not let him pass. So, Henry made the choice to camp at the apex of a roughly triangular-shaped field between dense woods that ran down either side of it. He decided to wait there and sit it out. That night, it poured down with rain and his men had to lie down in the cold and the mud. The next morning, on the 25th October (St Crispin's Day) the French lost patience and several thousand knights charged up the field to crush his small band of men. As the flaying hooves of the horses and points of the knights' lances bore down to rip his foot soldiers to pieces, King Henry V gave a signal and his archers let fly with their Yew tree Long Bows. Yew wood is very strong and springy and it allowed the cords attached to the Long Bows to stretch the wood right back. This meant that their arrows were launched long and high into the sky and plummeted down with such a speed and such a force that their tips penetrated even the thickest armour. It is reported, mum had told them, that the sky turned black with the arrows that rained down and then the ground turned red as they sliced through the armour of the charging French knights.

The knights were brought down in waves, but much worse was to follow. During the night, Henry had astutely told his archers to cut tree branches and sharpen both ends. He instructed that, when the time came, they were to ram the stakes into the mud in front of them for protection from the stamping hooves of the giant shire horses and long lances of the knights. Those knights that had managed to get through the hail of arrows now found themselves hung up on the spiked wall of wooden stakes. Some horses reared up in front of the spikes and threw the knights off. Others became bogged down in mud from the previous night's heavy rainfall whilst thrashing around trying to turn away. At another signal from Henry, his men-at-arms then marched through the spiked barrier and unseated the knights with swinging broadswords. His archers ran amongst the downed riders to finish them off with spikes and mallets. Of the seven thousand French dead that were mutilated on the battlefield, many were noblemen. At the sight of this slaughter, the rest of the French army retreated and King Henry V and his men made it safely, without being further troubled, to the coast and home to England.

As well as the major part that the Yew tree had played in the victory, mum also told her children that one of King Henry's archers on that day was thought to have been an ancestor of her family. Poppy and St John felt a pride within themselves every time they saw a Yew tree thereafter.

"That's it. Here we are!" yelled St John. The station nameplate 'MARKET HARBOROUGH' drifted past their carriage window as the train slowly glided to a halt. St John's words snapped Poppy out of the memories of her mother's stories and she jumped up and grabbed her belongings. They tumbled out onto the platform and squinted in the glare of the sunshine as their eyes searched for the Aunt Kay whom they had never met. The train pulled out of the station and the platform cleared of people. The two stood there alone and uncertain what to do. Then they spotted a slim, blue-eyed woman, about thirty years old, dressed in white blouse and black jeans, hurrying down towards them.

"You must be Rose's kids," she shouted. "Sorry I'm late. It's that damned Pig. Could I get him into the wagon? Could I heck! The ratbag had found this lump of manky green bread in the field and he just blanked me out when I shouted him to leave it and come. Had to twist his ears to drag him away before he could sink his teeth into anything else."

The pair was dismayed. They were going to be travelling on a horse and wagon with some sort of man-eating boar in the back. They could not help but stare at Aunt Kay as she came towards them. She had fair shoulder-length hair that appeared to be braided with twists of gold string. Aunt Kay saw them staring and tugged at it.

"Just look at that!" she exclaimed and pulled a handful of straw out of her hair. "I'll kill the little monster one day." She drew a finger across her throat in a gesture of mock execution. "I couldn't get the green, mouldy bread off him; he ate the lot, but it kept him occupied whilst I wrestled him to the field gate. Then he saw a hedgehog and chased it into a haystack. The last time he got hold of a hedgehog, he came back home with his face covered in fleas. I had to throw him in the river to get rid of them."

'That's a new one on me' thought St John. 'I didn't know that pigs could swim.'

"Anyway", continued Aunt Kay, "I managed to grab him round the neck this time, but not before he'd dragged me through the straw bales and given me this lot." She tugged at her hair again and more straw showered onto the platform. "Come on then kids," she laughed "Let's go!"

Aunt Kay picked up Poppy's bag and they marched down the platform. On the way, she gave them a ginger biscuit each. The starving St John went to eat his. "No, no," said Aunt Kay. "That's for the Pig. If you give him one of those, he will be your friend." They walked across the station car park, but not towards a horse and wagon. It was towards an old battered ex-army Land Rover. There, in the open back, was the Pig! He stood rigid, with tail straight out and scowled at anyone that came too close to the vehicle.

"It's a big black Labrador," shouted Poppy in surprise. "Why did you say it was a pig?"

"Because that's his name – Pig!" laughed Aunt Kay. "Pig by name, pig by nature; that's what I say. 'If it doesn't move – eat it!' that's his motto. So, he is as greedy as a pig. He'll chase anything; have a go at something five times his size; sees no danger whatsoever; totally ignores instructions and does what the hell he likes. That makes him pig-headed. So, could he have any other name, but Pig?" she asked the twins mischievously. Before they had a chance to answer she continued: "Mind you, he makes a wonderful guard dog and if you are his friend he will protect you to the death," said Aunt Kay proudly. "That is why I have given you the biscuits. I want him to be your friend and he will look after you whilst you are here."

Poppy and St John cautiously held out the ginger biscuits and Pig gobbled them down. As the kids were heaving a sigh of relief that they still had their hands left, he leaned forward and gave them a big sloppy lick up their cheeks. Poppy spluttered and dropped her notebooks in surprise. A man was passing by and innocently went to pick them up out of kindness, but immediately walked on when Pig's tail stood up, his body stiffened, his teeth bared and he snarled at him.

"There", said Aunt Kay. "He likes you. He is your friend and nobody will ever dare bother you."

All the way along the country lanes to the village of Tevlingorde, Pig happily sat in the open back of the old Land Rover, but every now and then he would stick his head through the back window into the cab and lick Poppy's ear. He would not stop until she gave him another ginger biscuit.

"There you are, I told you," tittered Aunt Kay. "Pig by name – pig by nature."

Their vehicle turned off the country road and down a single-track, dead-end lane. The track was lined with Whitebeam trees and the distinctive white underside of their fluttering leaves made it look like the glistening entrance to some sort of fairy dell. They entered the tiny village of Tevlingorde, turned left down Wishcot Lane and stopped at the very end outside an old thatched house that stood on its own. The nameplate above the oak door read: 'Wishcot Cottage'.

"Wishcot" murmured Poppy. "What a lovely name. Why is the lane called Wishcot?"

"Because the cows used to come down the lane twice a day to the parlour for milking," replied Aunt Kay.

"But what's that got to do with name Wishcot?" queried St John.

"The villagers have got a sly sense of humour," laughed Aunt Kay. "It's an anagram. You'll have to work it out for yourselves."

Behind the cottage were wheat fields. Straight on, Wishcot Lane turned into a stony cart track that meandered across green meadowland to a wooded hill in the distance.

"What's that?" asked Poppy, pointing at the steep rise in the land.

"That's Honeypot Hill," said Aunt Kay. "They say that sometimes a fuzzy glow can be seen coming from the woods on the top." Then, in a low, moaning voice, Aunt Kay whispered: "They say that it is hauuuuunted." Poppy looked at her quizzically. Then Aunt Kay laughed and they all started chuckling.

Something had also caught St John's eye. Off to the left of the cart track ran another track up to a solitary manor house. However, what had caught his attention was the large dome-shaped building at the side of it.

"That's a peculiar looking thing," said St John.

"Yes", agreed Aunt Kay. "That is where Professor Paul Poultney…"

She was halted by St John nearly being bowled over by Pig whizzing past his ear as he leapt out of the back of the vehicle and ran off down the cart track.

"As I was saying, before we were rudely interrupted by 'The flying Pig', that is where Professor Poultney lives. He retired down here recently. He is some sort of astronomer chappy and that's his observatory. Quite a clever man, I understand. He built the telescope himself. He is also very kind and friendly. That is where Pig will be off to now – to con a biscuit out of him!"

St John could not believe his luck. He held up his astronomy book written by Professor P. Poultney.

"Well, bless me," said Aunt Kay. "I didn't know you were interested in astronomy. Well, as I said, he is a nice chap. He often walks through the village. I'll introduce you and I'm sure he will show you around his observatory." St John was in heaven at the thought of such an opportunity.

The three of them entered Wishcot Cottage and Aunt Kay put the kettle on.

As Poppy looked out the window of her oak-beamed bedroom, she too, was in heaven. She could see an undulating sea of gold as the sun reflected off the breeze-blown wheat fields and further up the cart track rolled the emerald meadows to Honeypot Hill. 'How wonderful it would be to live here,' she thought. 'Away from the grey concrete housing estate where I come from.' Her eyes followed another path that she had spotted earlier leading off the cart track to the right. She looked enviously at a solitary white-walled farmhouse standing at the end of it. Aunt Kay had told Poppy that the old lady that lived there had died. It was not long after the death of her husband and villagers reckoned she had died of a broken heart. It had been standing empty for quite a while now. There had been a few well-to-do looking people come to eye it over – even though it had not been put up for sale. It was a big place. As well as the huge three-storey house with its further floor of sky-roof attic windows, courtyard and numerous outbuildings, there was a large area of land belonging to it. Its fields ran along the complete length of the cart track all the way down to Honeypot Hill and included the hill itself and the vast triangular meadowland that lay at its base. As Aunt Kay had pointed out:

"You would need a treasure chest full of gold to be able to buy that my girl!"

Poppy flopped onto her bed. It was a feather mattress and seemed to puff itself snugly around her. "Boy, I'll sleep well tonight," she sighed contentedly as she started to drift off into a daydream of being rich enough to buy the farmhouse up the track. A picture of herself standing at the honeysuckle-covered door feeding the ducks and dad walking home from working the fields drifted through her sleepy mind. In her dozing, she faintly heard Pig pad quietly into her bedroom and slink onto her bed. He lay on his back, with his head on the pillow next to hers and his legs sprawled in the air. She opened her eyes to see two large baby-brown eyes staring back at her. 'What a loving dog,' Poppy thought, as she reached out to stroke his silky ear.

Then, from downstairs, Aunt Kay shouted: "Dinner's ready!"

With that, Pig jumped up. A large paw squashed her nose and another dug into her stomach as he trampled over Poppy's head to be first down the stairs. The 'loving dog' had dumped her like a sack of spuds when the food came.

Poppy's shocked shout of: "You ignorant mutt!" followed the clatter of his claws down the polished wooden stairs. When she got down to the dining room, Pig was sitting next to her chair with his tail wagging, tongue hanging out and his lips pulled back in a way that seemed as if he was laughing. He was a rogue, but she could not stop herself from forgiving him.

They talked over dinner about themselves. Aunt Kay had told them that she was a freelance Chartered Accountant. She did a lot of work from home, but had taken a couple weeks off anyway to look after Poppy and St John. She had lost both parents in a car crash when she was very young. A distant relative, who in some way was related to Rose, the twin's mother, had brought her up. That is why she had taken the teenagers in now. Aunt Kay had lost her mum and she knew how they must feel. After dinner, they sat by the log fire whilst the pair talked about their harsh life in the city and the loss of their mother. Poppy proudly showed Aunt Kay her mum's sketchbooks and notes on wild flowers. St John sat on the floor at the fireside watching the logs glowing in the hearth, whilst Pig lay with his head in his lap. The young people began to yawn and finally, they slowly made their way up to bed.

Each was deep in personal thoughts. The past several months had been so traumatic for both of them that life had become an inescapable nightmare. The bullying they suffered at school had been a longstanding emotional torment, but the death of their wonderful, loving mother had been beyond endurance. It was as though every human pain and misery in the whole world had been gathered up, forged into a dagger then plunged deep into their hearts by an evil entity. As if that was not enough, dad had now taken ill and the twins were undergoing the stress of having to leave him behind. Compounding this was the upheaval of temporarily forsaking the home where the last vestiges of their mother's existence still gave them mute comfort.

Goodness knows what tomorrow would bring…?

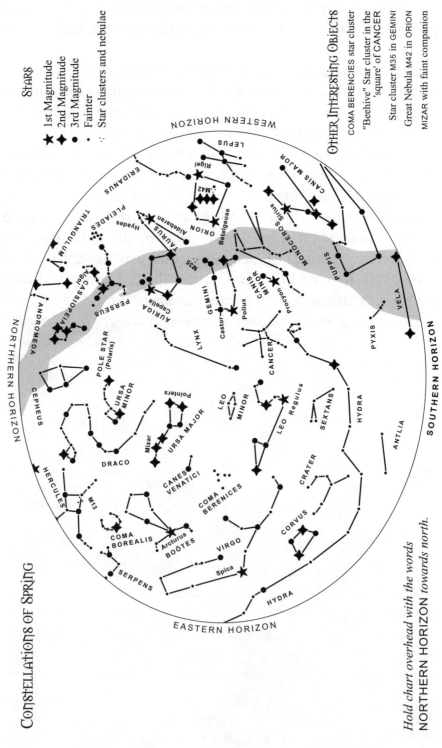

Constellations of Spring

Stars

★ 1st Magnitude
◆ 2nd Magnitude
● 3rd Magnitude
· Fainter
∴ Star clusters and nebulae

Other Interesting Objects

COMA BERENICES star cluster
"Beehive" Star cluster in the 'square' of CANCER
Star cluster M35 in GEMINI
Great Nebula M42 in ORION
MIZAR with faint companion

Hold chart overhead with the words
NORTHERN HORIZON *towards north.*

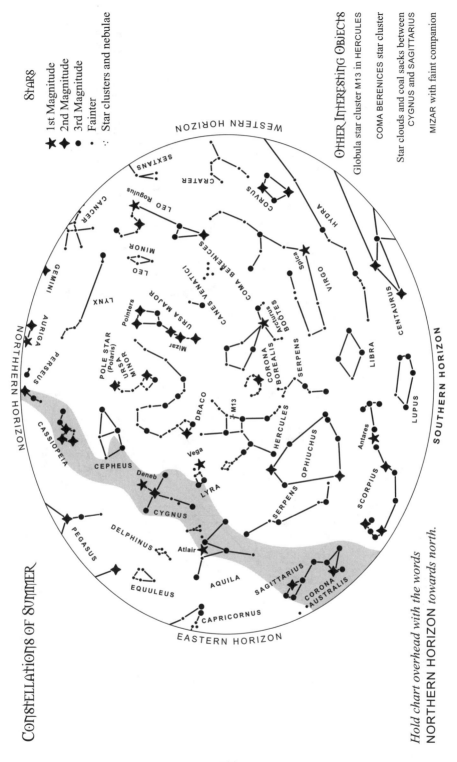

Constellations of Summer

Hold chart overhead with the words
NORTHERN HORIZON *towards north.*

Stars

★ 1st Magnitude
◆ 2nd Magnitude
● 3rd Magnitude
· Fainter
⁘ Star clusters and nebulae

Other Interesting Objects

Globula star cluster M13 in HERCULES

COMA BERENICES star cluster

Star clouds and coal sacks between CYGNUS and SAGITTARIUS

MIZAR with faint companion

Constellations of Autumn

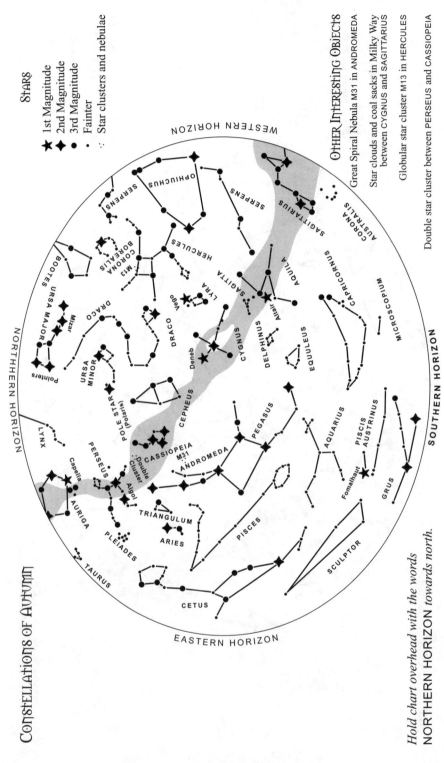

Stars

★ 1st Magnitude
✦ 2nd Magnitude
● 3rd Magnitude
· Fainter
∴ Star clusters and nebulae

Other Interesting Objects

Great Spiral Nebula M31 in ANDROMEDA

Star clouds and coal sacks in Milky Way between CYGNUS and SAGITTARIUS

Globular star cluster M13 in HERCULES

Double star cluster between PERSEUS and CASSIOPEIA

Hold chart overhead with the words
NORTHERN HORIZON *towards north.*

Constellations of Winter

Hold chart overhead with the words
NORTHERN HORIZON *towards north.*

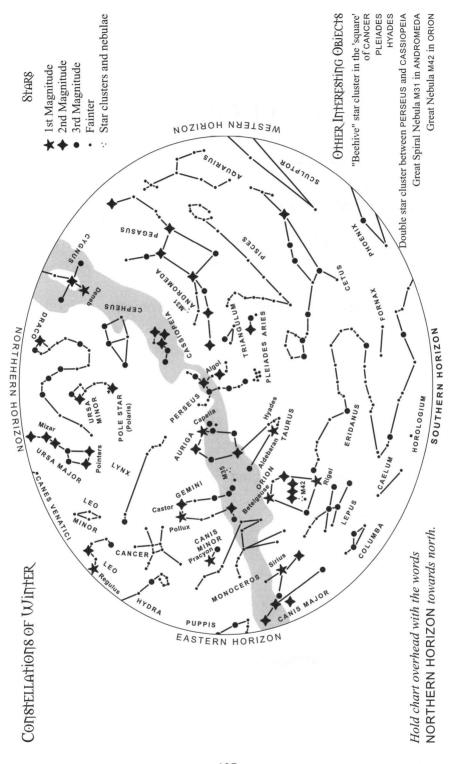

Stars

★ 1st Magnitude
◆ 2nd Magnitude
● 3rd Magnitude
· Fainter
⁛ Star clusters and nebulae

Other Interesting Objects

"Beehive" star cluster in the 'square'
   of CANCER
PLEIADES
HYADES
Double star cluster between PERSEUS and CASSIOPEIA
Great Spiral Nebula M31 in ANDROMEDA
Great Nebula M42 in ORION

Useful Contacts

For further information about the Wildflower Trilogy and its author, Paul Hayward, visit:

www.the-wild-flower-trilogy.com
www.flowers-of-the-gods.co.uk
www.children-of-the-stars.co.uk
www.a-bunch-of-wild-flowers.co.uk

For further information about astronomy you can contact:

National Space Centre
Exploration Drive
Leicester
LE4 5NS
Telephone: 0166 261 0261
Email: info@spacecentre.co.uk
Web: www.spacecentre.co.uk

For further information about British wild flowers you can contact:

Plantlife International
14 Rollestone Street
Salisbury
Wiltshire
SP1 1DX
Telephone: +44 (0) 1722 342730
Fax: +44 (0) 1722 329035
Email: enquiries@plantlife.org.uk
Web: www.plantlife.org.uk